Limited First Edition

Published by
Andrew Mellon
How to Shop
7-11 Gallowhill Street
Banff
Banffshire
AB45 1HA
Scotland
UK

This first edition published in 2008

Text copyright © Andrew Mellon 2008
Photography copyright © Keiko Oikawa 2008
Additional photography © Danny Elewes 2007

A CIP catalogue record of the book is available from the British Library

ISBN: 978 0 9560629 0 1

Printed and bound in Italy by Sedit SpA.
Print Management by Weygraphic Ltd

Every effort has been made to verify the information at the time of going to press.
The views and judgements are the opinion of the author, who accepts
no responsibility for mis-information or errors in the text.

HOW to SHOP

THE SERIOUS GUIDE FOR THE SERIOUS SHOPPER

HOW
SHOP
TO

THE SERIOUS GUIDE FOR THE SERIOUS SHOPPER

ANDREW MELLON

Foreword

It has taken my team and I months of painstaking research to provide the most up-to-date and relevant information that will be invaluable to the serious bargain hunter today.

During the past twenty years or so that I have been pounding the pavements searching for that 'best possible price', important changes have taken place in the retail industry. There has been an unprecedented growth in outlet shopping villages and they have increased by a massive tenfold since the eighties. Currently, there are more than forty outlet villages spanning the length and breadth of the UK. Historically, outlets have carried last seasons' fashions, discounted products, seconds and customer returns; however, these centres have now become so integral to the shopping experience, many manufacturers are producing stock specifically to be sold at outlets.

Inside these pages you'll find information on outlet villages, independent warehouse shops, the best sales, sample sales and internet shopping sites, alongside a comprehensive index to help you find the location of your favourite brands.

The three international shopping city guides not only give you great, up-to-the-minute shopping information, but advise on getting there, accommodation and local transport.

Like everyone else, I love a good bargain and if this guide helps people buy something that previously, they thought was way out of their reach, then it was well worth the writing.

If you have any comments, thoughts or suggestions that might make the next edition of this guide even better, it would be great to hear from you.

Happy shopping!

Andrew

Andrew Mellon
Autumn 2008.

Contents

Top 100 Independent Outlet Shops

This section of the book contains a wide selection of the best outlet shops across the country. Many are located on industrial estates or are tucked away off the beaten track, but they all have one thing in common: each offers great value for money. Every one has been individually reviewed and rated. Our star rating (from 1 to 5) gives you a clear indication of the selection, discount, quality of the goods and overall service. Many of these have additional savings on top of the outlet price at certain times of year. We recommend joining the mailing lists of your favourite outlets to receive advanced notification of sales and special discounts.

Alan Paine ★ ★

www.alanpaine.co.uk

The Cow House, Scats Countrystore Courtyard, Brighton Road, Godalming, Surrey, GU7 1NS

Telephone: 01483 419962

Opening Hours: Mon-Fri 9-5, Sat 9:30-5, Sun Closed

Customer parking is available and they accept credit cards.

This small shop sells a range of Alan Paine cashmere for men and women and some accessories with up to 50% off the original selling price.

Andrew Elliot ★ ★ ★

www.elliot-weave.co.uk

Forest Mill, Dunsdale Road, Selkirk, TD7 5EA

Telephone: 01750 720412

Opening Hours: Mon-Thurs 9-5, Fri 9-4, Sat & Sun Closed

Customer parking is available and they accept credit cards.

This outlet sells tweed fabric for men and women, along with a range of accessories at a discount of between 25% and 50% on seconds and end-of-line items.

Antler Ltd ★ ★

www.antler.co.uk

Pilot Works, Alfred St, Bury, Lancashire, BL9 9EF

Telephone: 01617 625000

Opening Hours: Sun-Fri 10-4, Sat 10-5

Customer parking is available and they accept credit cards.

This is Antler's warehouse shop which sells a range of old stock and samples at discounts of up to 70%. There are also Antler shops at many outlet villages.

Aquascutum ★ ★ ★

www.aquascutum.com

Unit 17, Princewood Rd, Earlstrees Ind Est, Corby, Northants, NN17 4AQ

Telephone: 01536 205086

Opening Hours: Mon-Fri 10-4:45, Sat 10-3:45, Sun Closed

Customer parking is available and they accept credit cards.

Also at: Cleveland Rd, Hemel Hempstead, Herts, HP2 7EY

Telephone: 01442 248333

Opening Hours: Mon-Sat 10-5, Sun Closed

Customer parking is available and they accept credit cards.

Aquascutum is known as a top quality outfitter for men and women with its two factory outlets selling past seasons' collections at up to 60% off.

Arthur Price ★ ★ ★

www.arthurprice.com
Britannia Way, Britannia Enterprise Park, Lichfield, Staffordshire,
WS14 9UY
Telephone: 01543 257775
Opening Hours: Mon-Fri 9-5, Sat 10-1, Sun Closed
Customer parking is available and they accept credit cards.
Also at: Arthur Price Silversmiths, 12 Orgreave Drive, Sheffield,
S13 9NR
Telephone: 01142 694607
Opening Hours: Mon-Thurs 9-4, Fri 9-11, Sat & Sun Closed
Customer parking is available and they accept credit cards.
The outlet shops have a good selection of stainless and silver plate
cutlery and hollow-ware in seconds and firsts at up to 50% off.

Austin Reed Clearance Shop ★ ★

www.austinreed.co.uk
Station Rd, Thirsk, North Yorkshire, YO7 1QH
Telephone: 01845 573135
Opening Hours: Mon-Fri 9:30-6, Sat 9-6, Sun 10:30-4:30
Customer parking is available and they accept credit cards.
The men's high street retailer offers formal and casual men's clothing
from previous seasons at up to 70% off the original price.

Aynsley China ★ ★ ★

www.aynsley.co.uk
Portland Works, Sutherland Road, Stoke-on-Trent, ST3 1HS
Telephone: 01782 339400
Opening Hours: Mon-Sat 9-5, Sun 11-4
Customer parking is available and they accept credit cards.
The shop at Stoke offers great deals on discounted patterns along with
a range of giftware, with prices reduced by up to 50%.

Barker shoes ★ ★ ★

www.barker-shoes.co.uk
Station Rd, Earls Barton, Northampton, Northamptonshire, NN6 ONT
Telephone: 01604 810387
This traditional English shoe manufacturer has a shop at the factory
selling both men's and women's shoes at discounts of between
35% and 40%, alongside other contemporay brands.

The Battersea Candle Shop ★★★

100 York Rd, London, SW11 3RU
Telephone: 0207 2234444
Opening Hours: Mon-Sat 9:30-5:30, Sun 11-5
Parking is free.
This candle shop has taken over the old Price's Candle factory shop and still offers varying discounts on a range of candles, including Price's, Flames and Church's.

Belinda Robertson ★★★★

www.belindarobertson.com
13a Dundas St, Edinburgh, Scotland, EH3 6QG
Telephone: 0131 5578118
Opening Hours: Mon-Sat 9-6, Sun 12-4
There is no customer parking but there is a pay and display nearby. They do accept credit cards. The basement of the Edinburgh Shop has a sale shop, selling end-of-lines and one off samples at discounts of up to 60%. They also have great sales in their London store and online. Join the mailing list to get regular updates and special offers.

Berry Brothers & Rudd ★★★

www.bbr.com
Hamilton Close, Houndmills, Basingstoke, Hants, RG21 6YB
Telephone: 01256 340132
Opening Hours: Mon-Thurs 10-6, Fri 10-7, Sat & Sun 10-4
Customer parking is available and they accept credit cards.
The outlet shop is at the Basingstoke warehouse and has a good selection of wines that are reduced because they are bin ends, surplus to requirements or fully mature. Discounts vary but most have at least 25% off. Join the mailing list to be kept up-to-date.

Browns Labels For Less ★★★★

www.brownsfashion.com
50 South Molton St, London, W1K 5RD
Telephone: 0207 5140052
Opening Hours: Mon-Sat 10-6:30, Sun Closed
There is no customer parking but they do accept credit cards.
Browns' sale shop has a good selection of both men's and women's previous seasons, at up to 75% off the original selling price, with many smaller designers represented.

Burberry ★★★

www.burberry.co.uk
Kitty Brewster Industrial Estate, Blyth, Northumberland, NE24 4RG
Telephone: 01670 352524
Opening Hours: Mon-Sat 10-5, Sun Closed
Customer parking is available and they accept credit cards.

Also at: Coronation Mills, Albion St, Castleford, West Yorkshire, WF10 1QX
Telephone: 01977 554411
Opening Hours: Mon-Sat 10-5, Sun Closed
Customer parking is limited but they do accept credit cards.
The Burberry Factory shops sell mostly the same stock as the outlets shops, but you can also find items that are samples and one offs. Well worth a visit for savings of up to 60%.

Burleigh ★★★
www.burleigh.co.uk
Middleport Pottery, Port St, Burslem, Stoke-on-Trent, Staffordshire, ST6 3PE
Telephone: 01782 577866
Opening Hours: Mon-Sat 9-5, Sun 10-4
Customer parking is available and they accept credit cards.
Burleigh are the only factory left still using the under-glaze technique on their pottery. A large selection of items can be found at their factory shop with discounts of up to 75%.

Caroline Charles ★★★★
www.carolinecharles.co.uk
18 Hill Rise, Richmond, Surrey, TW10 6UA
Telephone: 0208 487777
Opening Hours: Mon-Sat 10-5:30, Sun 11-4
There is no customer parking but they do accept credit cards.
This small women's high-end fashion chain have 10 shops that send the previous seasons' stock to their Richmond sale shop to be sold at discounts of 50% and upwards. Join the mailing list to receive special offers and extra discount cards.

Caspian Sea Caviar ★★★★
(mail order/phone orders only)
www.caspianseacaviar.com
Telephone: 01746 712307
Caspian provide a fast mail order service for all types of caviar starting with 50 gram tins. There are savings of up to 70% off food hall prices without compromising the quality. This is a great resource for that special occasion. Orders are sent mainly by special delivery in cold boxes. If you live in London same day delivery is available.

Chomette Domberger ★★★★
www.chomette.co.uk
307 Merton Road, London, SW18 5JS
Telephone: 0208 8777000
Chomette is the country's leading kitchen accessories importer; with cookware, French white porcelain and glass at discounts of 25%, 50% and 75%. You can join the mailing list to be updated with clearances and special offers.

Christopher Wray Lighting ★ ★ ★
www.christopherwray.com
600 Kings Rd, London, SW6 2YW (sale shop opposite flagship shop on Kings Rd)
Telephone: 0207 7518701
Opening Hours: Mon-Sat 9-6, Sun Closed
Customer parking is available behind the main store and they accept credit cards.
Christopher Wray has undergone a complete transformation and has closed some shops; as a result this sale shop opposite the flagship store sells ex-display, end-of-lines and some display pieces at discounts of up to 75%.

Churchill China Factory Outlet ★ ★ ★
www.churchillchina.com
Whieldon Rd, Stoke-on-Trent, Staffordshire, ST4 4HQ
Telephone: 01782 845097
Opening Hours: Mon-Sat 9-5, Sun 10-4
Customer parking is available and they accept credit cards.
Churchill, famous for hotel and catering chinaware, has a very large selection of hotel china alongside its home collection at amazing prices of up to 90% reductions.

Church's Shoes (factory shoe store) ★ ★ ★ ★
www.church-footwear.com
Spencer St, St James Rd, Northampton, Northamptonshire, NN1 5JB
Telephone: 01604 593313
Opening Hours: Mon-Fri 9:30-4:30, Sat 9:30-2, Sun Closed
Customer parking is available and they accept credit cards.
Church's are now owned by Prada, but this shop has a good selection of classic shoes with reductions of up to 60% off.

Contract Candles ★ ★ ★ ★ ★
www.contractcandles.com
Lower Lodge, Vann Rd, Fernhurst, Haslemere, Surrey, GU27 3NH
Telephone: 01428 645433
Opening Hours: Mon-Fri 9-5:30, Sat 10-4, Sun Closed
Customer parking is available and they accept credit cards.
The country's leading candle maker has a fantastic shop selling its end-of-lines, overruns and samples at amazing prices; hence the 5 star rating.

Cotswold Rock Bottom ★ ★ ★ ★

www.cotswoldoutdoor.com
Holyhead Rd, Betws-y-Coed, Gwynedd, LL24 0AP
Telephone: 01690 710234
Opening Hours: Sun-Thurs 9-6:30, Fri-Sat 9-7
Customer parking is available and they accept credit cards.
Also at: Former Lamb Inn, Red Lion Square, Grasmere, Cumbria, LA22 9SP
Telephone: 01539 435778
Opening Hours: Everyday 9:30-6
There is no customer parking but there are car parks & pay and
display nearby. They do accept credit cards.
You can find everything here for outdoor pursuits at discounts of up to 50% off the original price;
including camping, hiking and water sports gear.

Covent Garden Flower Market ★ ★ ★

www.cgma.gov.uk
New Covent Garden Market, London, SW8 5NX
Telephone: 0207 7202211
Opening Hours: Mon-Fri 3am-11am, Sat 4am-10am (NB not all wholesalers open on Sat), Sun Closed
Customer parking is available at a cost of £4. They don't accept credit cards and operate a cash only
policy.
The market is mainly for wholesale customers, but the public can shop here too. It has a great
selection and is a wonderful resource for larger occasions. Your final bill will be subject to VAT, and
payment is by cash only, unless you have an account.

Crockett and Jones ★ ★ ★ ★

www.crockettandjones.co.uk
Perry St, Northampton, Northamptonshire, NN1 4HN
Telephone: 01604 631515
Opening Hours: Fri 2-5:15, Sat 9:30-1:15
Customer parking is available and they accept credit cards.
This traditional shoemaker, in the heart of Britain's shoe making region, specialises in making
Goodyear welted shoes; mainly for men but with some women's styles too. Discounts of up to 60%.

Dar Lighting ★ ★ ★

www.darlighting.co.uk
Wildmere Road, Wildmere Industrial Estate, Banbury, OX16 3JZ
Telephone: 01295 672248
Quality seconds, plus samples of both traditional and contemporary lighting are available here at
greatly reduced prices.

Dartington Crystal ★ ★ ★

www.dartington.co.uk

Linden Close, Torrington, Devon, EX38 7AN

Telephone: 01805 626262

Opening Hours: Mon-Fri 9:30-5, Sat 10-5, Sun 10-4

Customer parking is available and they accept credit cards.

Also at: C/O Denby Pottery Co, Pottery Lane, Denby, Ripley, Derbyshire, DE5 8NX

Telephone: 01773 513116

Opening Hours: Mon-Sat 9-5, Sun 10-5

Customer parking is available and they accept credit cards.

The small outlet shop at Dartington Crystal has a good selection of discontinued stock and some seconds. Discounts of up to 50%.

David Oliver Designer Outlet ★ ★

45 Steep Hill, Lincoln, Lincolnshire, LN2 1LU

Telephone: 01522 532239

Opening Hours: Mon-Sat 10-6, Sun Closed

There is no customer parking available but they do accept credit cards.

This outlet sells women's designer collections and some accessories at a discount of up to 60%, and has a good selection of sizes.

Denby Pottery ★ ★ ★

www.denby.co.uk

Denby Visitor Centre, Factory shop and Home Store, Derby Rd, Denby, Derbyshire, DE5 8NX

Telephone: 01773 740700

Opening Hours: Mon-Sat 9:30-5, Sun 11-5

Customer parking is available and they do accept credit cards.

Also at: Boundary Mill Stores, Burnley Rd, Colne, Lancashire, BB8 9NW

Telephone: 01282 865229

Opening Hours: Mon-Fri 10-8, Sat 10-6, Sun 11-5

Boundary Mill Stores, Shiremoor, Park Lane, Newcastle-upon-Tyne, Tyne and Wear, NE27 OBS

Telephone: 01912 972420

Opening Hours: Mon-Fri 10-8, Sat 9-6, Sun 10-5

The Broadmarsh Centre, 202 Drury Walk, Nottingham, Nottinghamshire, NG1 7LR

Telephone: 0845 3137505

Opening Hours: Mon 9-5:30, Tue 9:30-5:30, Wed-Sat 9:30-5:30, Sun 10:30-4:30

The full collection of Denby's pottery is available in both first quality and seconds at a discount of up to 50%.

Denner Cashmere ★ ★ ★

www.dennercashmere.co.uk

BEMCO Building, Jews Row, London, SW18 1TB

Telephone: 0870 2200058

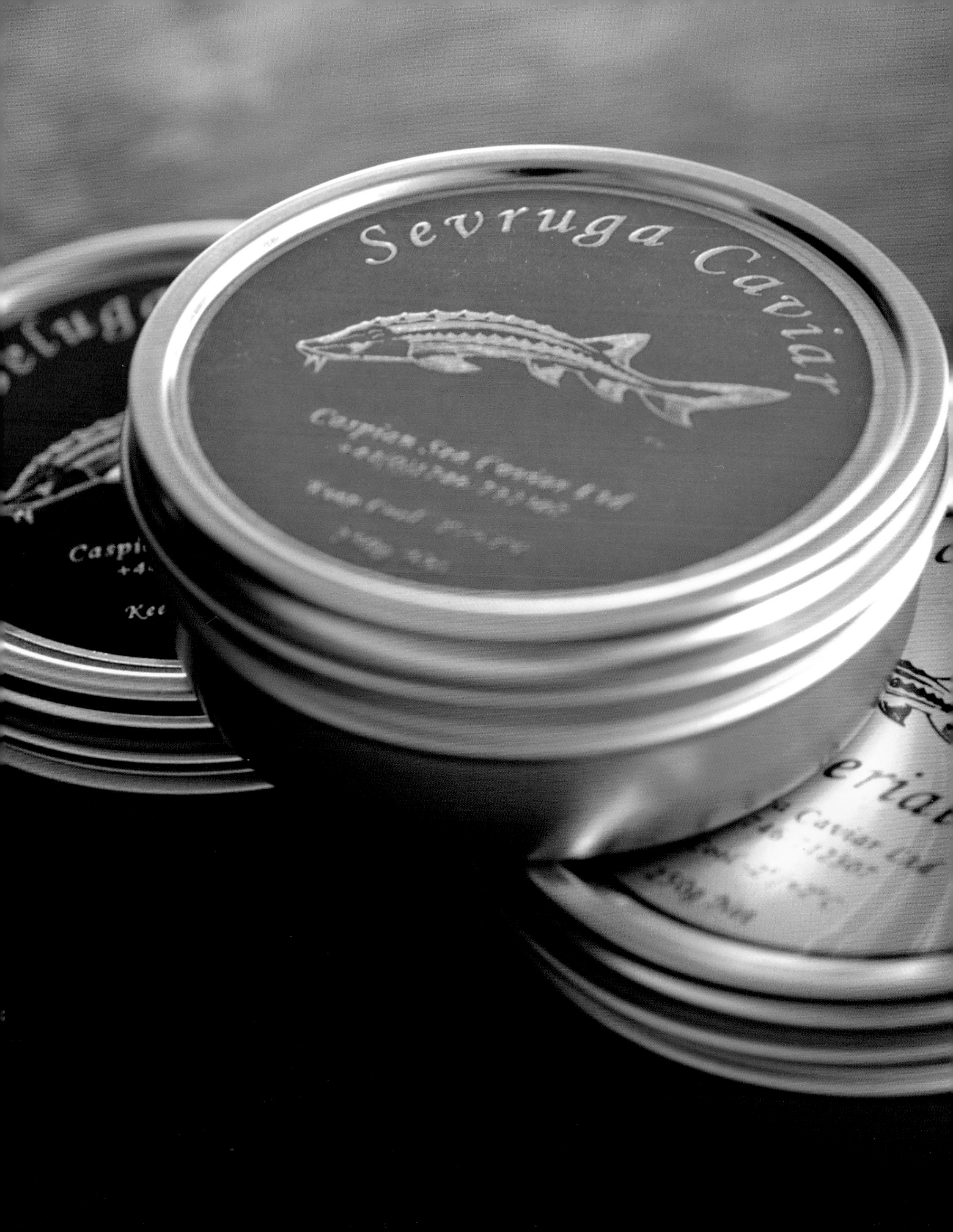
Sevruga Caviar
Caspian Sea Caviar Ltd

Opening Hours: Thurs Only
This small mail-order cashmere company opens on a Thursday to the public and sells end-of-line men's and women's cashmere at up to 75% discount. They also have a couple of sales a year. Join their mailing list to be kept updated.

Dents ★ ★ ★ ★ ★
www.dents.co.uk
12 Fairfield Rd, Warminster, Wiltshire, BA12 9DL
Telephone: 01985 217367
Opening Hours: Mon-Sat 9:30-5:30, Sun Closed
Customer parking is available and they do accept credit cards.
Dents are the leading accessories manufacturer in the UK. Merchandise includes women's and men's gloves for every occasion, leather goods, and a selection of handbags at discounts of between 20% and 50%. Log on to www.dents.co.uk to join the mailing list and for details of special sales and events.

Dexam International Ltd ★ ★ ★ ★
www.dexam.co.uk
Unit 8, Holmbush Ind Estate, Midhurst, Sussex, GU29 9HX
Telephone: 01730 814188
Opening Hours: Mon-Fri 9-4:45, Sat 10-1, Sun Closed
Customer parking is available and they accept credit cards.
This kitchen importer has an amazing collection of kitchenalia and also imports Chasseur cookware. Most lines are discounted between 30% and 70%. There are monthly promotions on selected lines with an extra 20% off.

Dible and Roy ★ ★ ★ ★
14-18 The Parade, Marlborough, Wiltshire, SN8 1NE
Telephone: 01672 513491
Opening Hours: Mon-Fri 8:30-5:15
Customer parking is available and they do accept credit cards.
This traditional home furnishing emporium always has an amazing selection of fabrics at discounts of up to 80%. They also have a branch at Bradford-upon-Avon.

Direct Cosmetics ★ ★ ★
www.directcosmetics.com
Telephone: Internet Only
This web-based company offers great discounts of cosmetics, skincare, beauty products and designer fragrances delivered to your door. A fantastic resource for discounted cosmetics.

Direct Electrical Sales ★ ★ ★ ★
www.directelectricalsales.co.uk
Unit 2, Fareham Enterprise Centre, Newgate Lane, Fareham, Hampshire, PO14 1TH

Telephone: 01329 319999
This wholesaler can offer trade pricing to personal callers on audio and visual equipment. Stock changes daily so it's worth visiting regularly to see what is available.

Doulton and Company ★ ★ ★
www.royaldoulton.com
Forge Lane, Stoke-on-Trent, Staffordshire, ST1 5NP
Telephone: 01782 284056
Opening Hours: Mon-Sat 9-6, Sun 9-5
Customer parking is available and they do accept credit cards.
The outlet shop at Doulton carries a full range of seconds and some discontinued firsts at reductions of up to 70%.

Duty Free ★ ★ ★ ★
www.worlddutyfree.com
The best buys we have found at duty free are the items in the boutique shops that are never normally discounted, such as ties, scarves, belts and accessories.

Emma Bridgewater ★ ★ ★ ★
www.emmabridgewater.co.uk
Eastwood Works, Lichfield St, Hanley, Stoke-on-Trent, Staffordshire, ST1 3EJ
Telephone: 01782 201328
Opening Hours: Mon-Sat 9:30-5:30, Sun 11-4
Customer parking is available and they do accept credit cards.
Bridgewater's signature pottery and kitchenware is available largely in the form of seconds, at discounts of up to 30%. The shop has additional sales in January and July.

Fired Earth Outlet ★ ★ ★
www.firedearth.co.uk
Twyford Mill, Oxford Rd, Adderbury, Banbury, OX17 3SX
Telephone: 01295 814399
Opening Hours: Mon-Sat 9:30-5:30, Sun 10-4
Customer parking is available and they do accept credit cards.
The factory shop receives end-of-lines and seconds in tiles, bathroom and kitchen furniture from Fired Earth's 56 UK shops. You can expect a discount of up to 60% with additional discounts during their sales.

Freelance Fabrics ★ ★ ★
www.freelancefabrics.com
4 Kidlington Centre, High St, Kidlington, OX5 2DL
Telephone: 01865 841088
Opening Hours: Mon-Sat 9-5, Sun 11-4
Customer parking is available and they do accept credit cards.
A huge range of furnishing fabrics is available at various discounts,
along with some craft supplies.

French Sole Shoes ★ ★ ★ ★
www.frenchsole.com
97 Queens Rd, Weybridge, Surrey, KT13 9UQ
Telephone: 01932 841717
Opening Hours: Mon-Sat 10-6, Closed Sun
Customer parking is not available but there is a pay and display nearby.
They do accept credit cards.
French Sole's signature ballet shoes from previous seasons are
available here. A selection of styles is available at 25% to 35% off.
Closed for lunch 2-3pm.

Fressingfield Pottery (Soendergaard Design) ★ ★ ★ ★
www.soendergaarddesign.co.uk
Fressingfield House, Church St, Fressingfield, Suffolk, IP21 5PA
Telephone: 01379 586200
Opening Hours: Open almost everyday, but call first to make sure
Customer parking is available and they do accept credit cards.
This tiny pottery factory produces a number of lines of hand thrown
pottery, including items for Nicole Farhi. A good selection of seconds is
always available. Call before you travel to confirm opening times.

GlenMuir Ltd ★ ★ ★
www.glenmuir.com
Delves Rd, Lanark, Lanarkshire, ML11 9DX
Telephone: 01555 662244
This golf clothing factory shop offers a great selection of branded golf
wear along with accessories at varying discounts.

Graham and Green ★ ★ ★
www.grahamandgreen.co.uk
Graham and Green do not have an outlet store but have a very good
online sale, with discounts of up to 50%.

Half Price Perfumes ★ ★ ★
www.halfpriceperfumes.co.uk
Half Price Perfumes have been in business since 1996, are UK based and ship goods within 24 hours. They carry over 100 brands at discount prices.

Hartley Greens Leeds Pottery Ltd ★ ★ ★
www.hartleygreens.fsbusiness.co.uk
Anchor Rd, Langton, Stoke-on-Trent, Staffordshire, ST3 5ER
Telephone: 01782 599959
Opening Hours: Mon-Thurs 8-4, Fri 8-2:30, Sat 10-2 (Sat Apr-Sept – other times by appointment only), Sun Closed
Customer parking is available and they do accept credit cards.
This factory shop sells slightly imperfect pieces from the complete range at greatly reduced prices. Delivery can be arranged. Factory tours are also on offer.

Hawick Cashmere Company ★ ★ ★
www.hawickcashmere.com
Trinity Mills, 11 Duke St, Hawick, Roxburghshire, TD9 9QA
Telephone: 01450 372510
Opening Hours: Mon-Sat 9:30-5, Sun Closed
Customer parking is available and they do accept credit cards.
The full range of the collection is available with certain lines reduced by up to 50%, including men's and women's clothing, scarves and gloves.

Jaeger ★ ★ ★
www.jaeger.co.uk
Unit 10, 19/23 Kings Walk, Kings St, Reading, Berkshire, RG1 2HG
Telephone: 01189 504699
Opening Hours: Mon-Sat 9:30-5:30, Sun Closed
Also at: Unit 13 Paxman Rd, Hardwick Ind. Estate, King's Lynn, Norfolk, PE30 4NE
Telephone: 01553 773840
Opening Hours: Mon-Fri 9:30-5:30, Sat 9:30-6, Sun 10:30-4:30
Customer parking is not available (lots of space in central Reading) and they do accept credit cards.
The two shops sell previous seasons' men's and women's wear at discounts of up to 60%.

James Gaunt ★ ★ ★
1 Church St, Frome, BA11 1PW
Telephone: 01373 452344
Opening Hours: Mon-Sat 9-5:30, Sun Closed
Customer parking is not available and they do accept credit cards.
This shop has very good prices on furnishing and curtain fabrics and a great sale twice a year where most of its £10 to £120 per metre fabric sells for £5 per metre.

Jo Malone ★★★★
www.jomalone.co.uk
Telephone: 0870 0342411
The shops at duty free in Terminals 3 and 5 at Heathrow offer around a 20% discount on the entire Jo Malone range. However, unlike other outlets within the terminal, you cannot leave your purchases for collection upon your return.

Joel & Son Fabrics ★★★
www.joelandsonfabrics.co.uk
73-85 Church St, London, NW8 8EU
Telephone: 0207 7246895
Opening Hours: Mon-Sat 9-5, Sun Closed
Customer parking is not available and they do accept credit cards.
Famous for bolts of designer clothing fabric. Great haberdashery department, with an amazing collection of buttons. Good discounts on older stock.

John Jenkins & Sons ★★★★★
www.johnjenkinsdirect.co.uk
Nyewood, Rogate, Petersfield, Hampshire, GU31 5HZ
Telephone: 01730 821811
Opening Hours: Mon-Sat 9:30-5
Customer parking is available and they do accept credit cards.
As one of the country's leading manufacturers of crystal and glass, the 3,000 square foot outlet shop sells seconds, discontinued glass and crystal along with gifts and a home collection. Discounts as much as 75% off. (Also see Top 10 Sales.)

John Lewis ★★★
www.johnlewis.com
Telephone: 0845 049049
Although a chain of department stores, we have listed John Lewis here as they have a good selection of slightly damaged white goods discounted throughout the year

John Smedley Ltd ★★★★
www.johnsmedley.com
Lea Mills, Lea Bridge, Matlock, Derbyshire, DE4 5AG
Telephone: 01629 534571
Opening Hours: Everyday 10-4
Customer parking is available and they do accept credit cards.
Also at: Rands Lane, Armthorpe, Doncaster, Yorkshire, DN3 3DY
(much smaller)
Telephone: 01302 832346
Opening Hours: Mon-Thurs 10-3:30, Fri & Sat 9:30-3
Customer parking is available and they do accept credit cards.

The two shops sell previous seasons' collections for men, women and children at reductions of up to 66%. You can also find factory samples at great prices.

Johnstons of Elgin ★ ★ ★
www.johnstonscashmere.com
New Mill, Elgin, Scotland, IV30 4AF
Telephone: 01343 554099
Opening Hours: Mon-Fri 9-6, Sat 9-5:30, Sun 11-5
Customer parking is available and they do accept credit cards.
The visitors' centre always has great reductions on scarves, gloves, and sweaters for men and women, along with some reductions on previous season's home collections. (Also see Top 10 Sales.)

Joseph Sale Shop ★ ★ ★ ★
www.joseph.co.uk
53 Kings Rd, London, SW3 4ND
Telephone: 02077 307562
Opening Hours: Mon-Sat 10-6, Wed 10-7, Sun 12-5
Customer parking is not available and they do accept credit cards.
This small shop sells last seasons' women's fashions at up to 90% reductions.

Kangol ★ ★ ★
www.kangolstore.co.uk
Armstrong Mills, 173 Charnwood Rd, Shepshed, Leicester, Leicestershire, LE12 9NN
Telephone: 01509 600006
Opening Hours: Mon-Sat 9:30-5:30, Sun 10:30-4:30
Customer parking is available and they do accept credit cards.
Also at: Bollman International, Cleator Mills, Cleator, Cumbria, CA23 3DJ
Telephone: 01946 810312
Opening Hours: Mon-Sat 9-5, Sun Closed
Customer parking is available and they do accept credit cards.
This famous hat manufacturer for men and women sells hats in all shape and sizes. They have end-of-line and discontinued stock. Kangol also sells some men's and women's clothing and various discounted Jane Shilton bags and shoes.

Kenwood ★ ★ ★
www.kenwoodworld.com/uk
New Lane, Havant, PO9 2NH.
Telephone: 02392 476000

Opening Hours: Mon-Sat 9-4:30 (closed 1-1.30)
Customer parking is available and they do accept credit cards.
You can find most of the Kenwood range at the outlet shop, alongside older stock at discounts of up to 60% off the RRP. Their postcode does not work reliably in sat-navs, so they advise using: New Lane, Havant.

Kidderminster Wholesale Carpets ★ ★ ★
Unit 1-2, Long Meadow Mills Ind. Estate, Dixon St, Kidderminster, Worcestershire, DY10 1HH
Telephone: 01562 60811
Opening hours: Mon-Sat 9:30-5 Sun 11-4
This outlet stocks the higher end of the high street carpets. If they do not have the carpet you want, they will get it for you at discounts of up to 40% off the high street price. There are 5 other carpet shops in Kidderminster.

Lakeland ★ ★ ★
www.lakeland.co.uk
11 Wharton Street (off The Hayes), Cardiff, CF10 1AG
Telephone: 02920 235050
Opening Hours: Mon-Sat 9-5:30
Customer parking is not available, other than Pay and Display in the multi storey, and they do accept credit cards.
Lakeland, who are best known for mail order, have a good sale. Their Cardiff store also has a large second floor clearance section with discontinued and slightly damaged lines at discounts of up to 70%.

Land's End Direct Merchants ★ ★ ★
www.landsend.co.uk
Unit 27d, The Pavilion, The Bishop Centre, Bath Rd, Taplow, Maidenhead, Berkshire, SL6 0NX
Telephone: 01628 602804
Opening Hours: Mon 10-6, Tues-Fri 9:30-6, Sat 9-6, Sun 10-4
Customer parking is available and they do accept credit cards.
Also at: Land's End Way, Oakham, Rutland, LE15 6US
Telephone: 01572 758014
Opening Hours: Mon-Sat 10-6, Sun 10-4
Customer parking is available and they do accept credit cards.
This American mail order company has two outlets selling casual and outdoor clothing for men and women at up to 75% of the original price.

Linton Tweeds ★ ★ ★
www.lintontweeds.co.uk
Shaddon Mills, Shaddongate, Carlisle, Cumbria, CA2 5TZ
Telephone: 01228 527569
Opening Hours: Mon-Sat 9:30-4:30, Sun Closed

Linton manufacture some spectacular tweeds for the couture labels and the unused bolts are returned and sold in the outlet shop for between £15 to £30 per metre.

LK Bennett ★★★
www.lkbennett.com
239 Kings Road, Chelsea, London, SW3 5EJ
Telephone: 0207 3764108
The outlet shop is selling the clothing collection, shoes and accessories for women at discounts starting at 50% and going up to as much as 70%.

Lloyd Loom of Spalding ★★
www.lloydloom.com
Wardentree Lane, Pinchbeck, Spalding, Lincolnshire, PE11 3UG
Telephone: 01775 712111
Opening Hours: Mon-Thurs 8:30-5, Fri 8:30-4, Sat 10-4, Sun Closed
Customer parking is available and they do accept credit cards.
There has been quite a revival in Lloyd Loom furniture and the outlet shop has a good selection, including bedroom furniture, sofas and their classic chairs at reductions of up to 50%.

Lombok Clearance & White Company ★★★★
www.lombok.co.uk
Unit 2, The Gasworks, 2 Michael Rd, London, SW6 2AD
Telephone: 0207 7365171
Opening Hours: Thurs-Sat 10-6, Sun 11-5
Customer parking is available and they do accept credit cards.
The ever-changing home accessories and furniture collection at Lombok stocks sample products, discontinued, and slightly damaged products with discounts of up to 70%.
A mailing list can be joined to benefit from exclusive discounts.

Magic Mountain ★★★
www.magic-mountain.co.uk
Howard Town Mill, off Victoria St, Glossop, Derbyshire, SK13 8HT
Telephone: 01457 854424
Opening Hours: Tues-Fri 9-5, Sat, 9:30-5, Sun & Mon Closed
Customer parking is available and they do accept credit cards.
The factory shop has a good selection of mountaineering and running gear along with Sprayway coats. Everything is discounted by at least 50% off the retail price.

Mamas & Papas ★★★★
www.mamasandpapas.co.uk
Colne Bridge Rd, Huddersfield, Yorkshire, HD5 0RH
Telephone: 0845 2682000

Opening Hours: Mon-Sat 9-5:30, Thurs 9-7, Sun 10-4
Customer parking is available and they do accept credit cards.
Also at: The Octagon Retail Park, Hanley, Stoke-on-Trent, ST1 5RR
Telephone: 0870 8307700
Opening Hours: Mon-Fri 10-6, Thurs 10-8, Sat 9:30-6, Sun 10:30-4:30
Customer parking is available and they do accept credit cards.
The two factory shops stock a range of furniture, clothing and maternity
goods, which are either discontinued or seconds, at discounts of up
to 33%.

Marston & Langinger ★★★

www.marston-and-langinger.com
192 Mozart Terrace, Ebury St, London, SW1W 8UP
Telephone: 020 78815700
The outlet shop in Norfolk has closed, but a fantastic sale happens in
the London store in January, which offers discounts of up to 70% off
furniture, garden accessories and outdoor dining products.

Marshall Leisure ★★★

www.marshallleisure.co.uk
Scremerston, Berwick-upon-Tweed, Northumberland, TD15 2QT
Telephone: 01289 309090
Opening Hours: Mon-Sat 9-6, Sun 10-4
Customer parking is available and they do accept credit cards.
Marshall Leisure stocks camping equipment and a good selection of
outdoor clothing by various manufacturers. Also available on the web.

Montane ★★★

www.montane.co.uk
Unit 21 Freeman Court, North Seaton Ind Estate, Ashington, Newcastle,
NE63 0YB
Telephone: 01670 522300
Opening Hours: Thurs & Fri 9-5, Sat 9-4
Customer parking is available and they do accept credit cards.
Montane sells outdoor performance clothing for running, biking, hiking
and climbing at various discounts.

Moorcroft Pottery ★★

www.moorcroft.com
Phoenix Works, Nile St, Cobridge, Stoke-on-Trent, Staffordshire, ST6 2BH
Telephone: 01782 820500
Opening Hours: Mon-Fri 10-5, Sat 9:30-4:30, Sun Closed
Customer parking is available and they do accept credit cards.

Moorcroft's lamps and vases are available as seconds at a discount of around 20%. Join the collectors club to save an additional 10%.

Mulberry Factory Shop ★ ★ ★ ★

www.mulberry.com
The Old School House, Kilver Street, Shepton Mallet, Somerset, BA4 5NF
Telephone: 01749 340583
Opening Hours: Mon-Sat 10-6, Sunday 11-5
Customer parking is available and they do accept credit cards.
Mulberry's outlet shop sells the company's leather collections, including signature luggage, and men's and women's small leather goods. The outlet also stocks a selection of clothing for both sexes. All products are discounted by up to 30%.

Multiyork ★ ★ ★

www.multiyork.co.uk
Clearance stores: Bath, Bournemouth, Canterbury, Eastbourne, Lincoln, Manchester, Mellis, Northampton, Reading, Redbrick Mill, Salisbury, and Watford
Telephone: 01842 764761
The 12 branches of Multi York highlighted above have clearance areas; however, the main clearance centre is at the Old Mill, Mellis, nr. Eye, Suffolk, IP23 8DW.

New Balance Athletic Shoes UK Ltd ★ ★ ★

www.newbalance.co.uk
Market Square, Main St, Shap, Penrith, Cumbria, CA10 3NL
Telephone: 01931 716333
Opening Hours: Mon-Fri 9:30-5:30, Sat 9-5, Sun 10-4
Customer parking is available and they do accept credit cards.
Also at: St Helens Lane, Workington Road, Flimby, Maryport, Cumbria, CA15 8RY
Telephone: 01900 602850
Opening Hours: Mon-Fri 9:30-5:30, Sat 9-5, Sun 10-4
Customer parking is available and they do accept credit cards.
15 Bank St, Keswick, Cumbria, CA12 5JY
Telephone: 01768 774631
Opening Hours: Mon-Sat 9-6, Sun 10-5
Customer parking is not available however there is a pay and display nearby and they do accept credit cards.
This performance brand's outlet shop sells athletic shoes, along with men's and women's clothing at discounts of up to 30%.

Nicholas Mosse ★ ★ ★

www.nicholasmosse.com
Bennettsbridge, County Kilkenny
Telephone: 00353 (0)56 7727505

Opening Hours: Mon-Sat 10-6, Sun 1:30-5
Customer parking is available and they do accept credit cards.
A small space in this converted mill is given over to Nicholas Mosse's
seconds with discounts of up to 40% off.

OKA Discount Shop ★ ★ ★ ★
www.okadirect.com
25 West St, Haslemere, Surrey, GU27 2AP
Telephone: 01428 648644
Opening Hours: Mon-Sat 9:30-5:30, Sun 11-4
Customer parking is available and they do accept credit cards.
Also at: Vogue Industrial Park, Tower Road, Berinsfield, Wallingford,
Abingdon, OX10 7LN
Telephone: 01865 342309
Opening Hours: Mon-Sat 9:30-5:30, Sun 11-4
Customer parking is available and they do accept credit cards.
Unit 17, Farm Lane Trading Estate, 101 Farm Lane, London, SW6 1QJ
Telephone: 0207 4710760
The 3 outlet shops sell customer returns, slightly damaged and
discontinued lines at discounts of up to 70% off the retail price.

P J Bridgman ★ ★ ★
www.bridgman.co.uk
Barnbridge Works, 82 Lockfield Avenue, Brimsdown, Enfield, Middlesex,
EN3 7PX
Telephone: 0208 8047474
Opening Hours: Mon-Fri 10-4, Weekends Closed
Customer parking is available and they do accept credit cards.
This outdoor furniture designer and importer has a good selection of
conservatory furniture, outdoor tables, chairs and loungers at discounts
of between 30% and 80%.

Paul Costelloe Factory Store ★ ★ ★
www.paulcostelloe.com
The Workshop, 9 Linen Green, Main Road, Moygashel, Dungannon, Co
Tyrone, BT71 7HB, N Ireland
Telephone: 02887 753867
Opening Hours: Mon-Sat 9:30-5:30, Sun Closed
Customer parking is available and they do accept credit cards.
The outlet shop is a franchise, which enables the stock to be sold at a
lower price (mostly 30% discount). You can get up to 70% discount on
last seasons' stock.

Peruvian Connection ★★★★

www.peruvianconnection.co.uk
47 Bell Street, Henley-on-Thames, Oxfordshire, RG9 2BA
Telephone: 01491 414 446
Opening Hours: Mon-Sat 9:30-5:30
Customer parking is not available but there is parking at a nearby Waitrose and they do accept credit cards.
This luxury textile company has manufactured their natural fibre products since 1976. The company specialises in women's clothing but also produces a menswear collection. Their handmade knits, among other things, can be found here at discounts of between 30% and 70%.

Portmeirion ★★★

www.portmeirion.co.uk
473 King Street, Stoke-on-Trent, Staffordshire, ST3 1EU
Telephone: 01782 326664
Opening Hours: Mon-Fri 9-5:30, Sun 10-4
Customer parking is available and they do accept credit cards.
Sells both first collections and seconds of ceramic cookware, accessories, and textiles with a 30% discount on seconds.

Pringle Factory Shop ★★★

www.pringlescotland.com
Glebe Mill, Noble Place, Hawick, Lothian and Borders, TD9 9QE
Telephone: 01450 360279
Opening Hours: Mon-Sat 9-5
Customer parking is available and they do accept credit cards.
The factory shop sells different stock from the outlet village shops. Mostly samples, one offs and end-of-lines. There is lambswool and cashmere for the entire family at massive discounts.

Replay Factory Shop ★★★★

www.replay.it
147-149 Fulham Road, London SW3 6SD
Telephone: 0207 5892870
Opening Hours: Mon-Sat 10-6:30, Sun 12-6
Customer parking is not available but they do accept credit cards.
This outlet shop is in a prime position in Chelsea. It sells Replay jeans and casual clothing lines from previous seasons at 50% off for men, women, and children.

Royal Crown Derby ★★★

194 Osmaston Road, Derby, Derbyshire, DE23 8JZ
Telephone: 01332 712800
Opening Hours: Mon-Sat 10-5
Customer parking is available and they do accept credit cards.

This classic pottery has a small selection of seconds at the factory in Derby. The usual discount on seconds is 30%.

Royal Worcester ★ ★ ★
www.royalworcester.co.uk
Royal Worcester Bestware Shop, Royal Worcester, Severn Street, Worcester, WR1 2NE
Telephone: 01905 746000
Opening Hours: Mon-Sat 9-5:30, Sun 11-5
Customer parking is available and they do accept credit cards.
The factory shop has a great selection of Royal Worcester's collection, (both current and discontinued) with additional discounts available throughout the year. Museum and café on-site.

Sandpiper Books ★ ★ ★
www.sandpiper.co.uk
34 Kensington Gardens, Brighton, BN1 4AL
Telephone: 01273 605422
Opening Hours: Mon-Sat 10-5:30, Sun 11-5
Customer parking is not available but there is parking at nearby Churchill Square and they do accept credit cards.
This independent shop in The Lanes has a really good selection of coffee table books at great prices and a second hand section.

Sanderson Clearance (at Standfast) ★ ★
www.sanderson-uk.com
Standfast & Barracks, Caton Road, Lancaster, LA1 3PA
Telephone: 01524 598222
Opening Hours: Mon-Fri 9:30-2
This outlet replaces the larger Sanderson outlet shop and carries a much smaller collection of fabrics with good discounts.

Southern Domestic Electrical Services ★ ★ ★
2-6 Bridge Road, Woolston, Southampton, SO19 7GQ
Telephone: 02380 328428
Opening Hours: Mon-Fri 8:30-6, Sat 9-5, Sun 10-4
Customer parking is available and they do accept credit cards.
A good selection of white goods for the kitchen at discounts of up to 50% off. The items are reduced because of cosmetic damage during delivery, or because they are older stock.

Speedo International ★ ★ ★
www.speedo.com
Ascot Road, Nottingham, NG8 5AJ
Telephone: 0115 9167000
Opening Hours: Mon-Sat 10-5, Sun 11-4

Customer parking is available and they do accept credit cards. The factory shop has a large selection of the current and older collections for men, women and children at varying discounts.

Spode (Visitor Centre) ★ ★ ★ ★
www.spode.co.uk
Church Street, Stoke-on-Trent, Staffordshire, ST4 1BX
Telephone: 01782 744011
Opening Hours: Mon-Sat 9-5:30, Sun 11-5
Customer parking is available and they do accept credit cards. Spode has 3 shops at the factory: best, seconds and clearance. All have good discounts, but the clearance shop is the place for great buys at incredible prices. The seconds carry a 50% discount off full price.

Stuart Crystal ★ ★ ★
www.waterfordwedgwood.com
Muthill Rd, Crieff, Perthshire, PH7 4HQ
Telephone: 01764 654004
Opening Hours: Everyday 10-6
Customer parking is available and they do accept credit cards. The large outlet shop carries both the discontinued and current collection for Stuart. The discontinued patterns start at 30% off. First quality goes on promotion during sales periods.

The Real Flower Company ★ ★ ★ ★
www.realflowers.co.uk
Unit 2 Durleigh Marsh Farm, Petersfield, Hampshire, GU31 5AX
Telephone: 01730 818300
Opening Hours: Fri 9-5
Customer parking is available and they do accept credit cards. On a Friday you can buy the end of the week 'special' of two bunches of spectacular roses for £15.00, subject to availability. You can also order their beautiful flowers on-line or by mail order.

Threshers Wine Rack ★ ★ ★ ★ ★
www.threshergroup.com
Telephone: 01707 387200
Branches nationwide. We have found that Threshers have the most consistent prices for champagne with their 3 for 2 offer, which is confirmed to run until March 2009.

TK Maxx ★ ★ ★ ★ ★

www.tkmaxx.com
This is not an independent outlet shop, but its 226 branches each carry different products in clothing, shoes, accessories, home wares and gifts at unbelievable prices.

Toast ★ ★ ★

www.toast.co.uk
Ashmount Business Park, Upper Forest Way, Swansea Enterprise park, Swansea, West Glamorgan, SA6 8QR, Wales
Telephone: 08445 575200
Opening Hours: Mon-Fri 9:30-5:30, Sat 9:30-5, Sun 10:30-4
Customer parking is available but is limited and they do accept credit cards.
This lifestyle mail order and retail company's outlet shop has a good assortment of the previous seasons' home and clothing collections at varying discounts.

Tog 24 Outdoor Clothing ★ ★ ★

www.tog24.com
Unit 4, Market Cross, Ambleside, Cumbria, LA22 9BT
Telephone: 01539 433913
Opening Hours: Mon-Sat 9:30-5:30, Sun 10-5
Customer parking is not available but they do accept credit cards.
Also at: 9 Market Sq, Keswick, Cumbria, CA12 5BJ
Telephone: 01768 780876
Opening Hours: Mon-Sat 9:30-6, sun 10-5:30
Customer parking is not available but they do accept credit cards.
The outlets sell performance winter, ski and outdoor clothing at discounts of up to 50%. Tog 24 also has a good online sale.

Trade Secret ★ ★ ★

www.trade-secret.co.uk
Twyford Mill, Oxford Rd, Adderbury, Nr Banbury, Oxfordshire, OX17 3SX
Telephone: 01295 810110
Opening Hours: Mon-Sat 10-5, Thurs 10-7, Sun 11-4
Customer parking is available and they do accept credit cards.
Also at: Hartley Farm Business Park, Hartley Park Farm, Selbourne, Alton, Hants, GU34 3HS
Telephone: 01420 511690
Opening Hours: Mon-Sat 10-5, Sun 11-4
Customer parking is available and they do accept credit cards.
Unit 5, Hatch End Industrial Estate, Middle Aston, Oxfordshire, OX25 5QL
Telephone: 01869 347720
Opening Hours: Mon-Sat 10-5, Sun 11-4
Customer parking is available and they do accept credit cards.

The company now has 3 outlets and a very large selection of furniture at the high-end of the market. They sell returned and slightly damaged goods at reductions of up to 75%. It is a great place to pick up a furniture bargain. Now open at Sydenham.

Vallebona Ltd ★★★★
www.vallebona.co.uk
Unit 14, 59 Weir Rd, Wimbledon, London, SW19 8UG
Telephone: 0208 9445665
Opening Hours: Sat 9:30-4
Customer parking is available and they do accept credit cards.
This Italian import company opens its warehouse to the public on a Saturday to sample and purchase their amazing collection of charcuterie, cheeses, pastas, and wines. Savings of up to 50% off food hall prices.

Volga Linen ★★★
www.volgalinen.co.uk
15 South Entrance, Saxmundham, Suffolk, IP17 1DG
Telephone: 01728 633091
Opening Hours: Mon-Sat 10-5
Customer parking is available and they do accept credit cards.
There is a small sale section within the store selling previous collections of exquisite pure linens from Europe and Russia. It features table linen, bed linen and some clothes at various discounts.

Waterford Crystal ★★★
www.waterfordwedgwood.com
Muthill Rd, Crieff, Perthshire, PH7 4HQ
Telephone: 01764 654004
Opening Hours: Everyday 10-6
Customer parking is available and they do accept credit cards.
The large outlet shop carries both discontinued and current collections for Waterford. The discontinued patterns start at 30% off, and first quality goes on promotion during sale periods.

Wedgwood ★★★
www.wedgwood.com
King St, Fenton, Stoke-on-Trent, Staffordshire, ST4 3DQ
Telephone: 01782 316161
Opening Hours: Mon-Sat 9:30-5, Sun 11-5
Customer parking is available and they do accept credit cards.
The outlet shop at Wedgwood has a great selection of discontinued and seconds stock at varying discounts of up to 70%. Wedgwood also offers a good online sale.

CHAMPAGNE
MAISON FONDÉE EN 1772
Clicquot Ponsar
VINTAGE
1999
À REIMS-FRANCE

Wesley Barrell ★ ★ ★

www.wesley-barrell.co.uk
3 Bridge St, off High St, Witney, Oxfordshire, OX28 1BY
Telephone: 01993 776682
The Witney shop has a large clearance area of both classic and contemporary sofas, tables, chairs and lamp tables. Its constantly changing stock is made up of display items at discounts of between 30% and 60%.

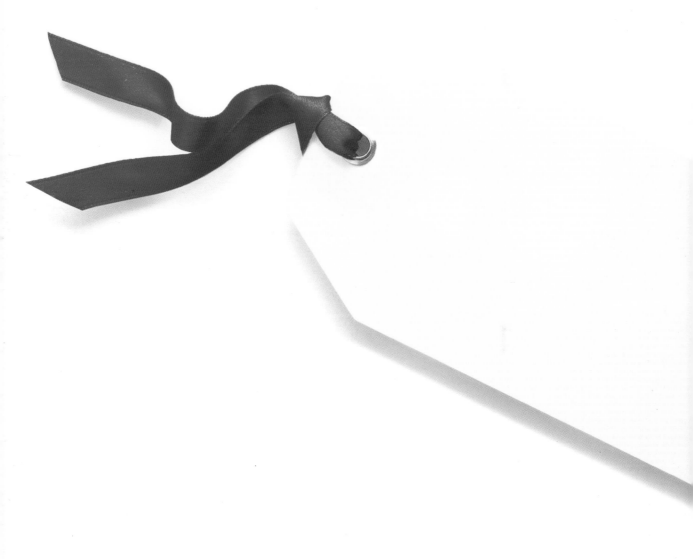

Top 10 Outlet
Shopping Villages

With some 45 outlet villages in the UK and with new ones opening (Gloucester quays in Spring 2009), we have reviewed what, in our opinion, are the 10 best outlet villages in the country. We have also reviewed the top 10 shops inside the villages that give you the best deals; based on quality, selection and discount, alongside location and contact information. A word of warning – unlike high street shops, which will give you a refund, outlets will only exchange your items or give you credit. We also advise calling ahead if you are going to a particular store as outlet shops have been known to be there one minute and gone the next!

1. Bicester Village

50 Pingle Drive, Oxon, OX26 6WD
Telephone: 01869 323200
www.bicestervillage.com

Opening Hours:
Mon, Tues, Wed and Sun 10-6
Thurs-Sat 10-7

Bicester is considered by many to be the country's best outlet village, hence its position as our number one UK outlet village. Because of its incredible reputation, (many top designers have their one and only outlet shop here) we have reviewed 30 shops for you. However, it would be fair to say that there are over 100 stores in the village that offer excellent buys and 28 new retail units are set to open in Autumn 2008. A number of new restaurants will be joining the already busy Carluccio's, Pret A Manger and Starbucks who have concessions at Bicester. Join the mailing list (www.bicestervillage.com) or telephone to receive updates and a free VIP card twice a year, which gives you a further 10% discount. Located at Junction 9 of the M40 and just off the A34.

How to get there

By Car – take the M40 to exit 9. Follow signs to the Village Retail Park and Bicester Village. Parking is free.

By Bus – Stagecoach offer a daily service every half hour to Bicester Village from Magdalen Street in Oxford (outside Debenhams).

By Train – up to four trains an hour from London Marylebone, or Birmingham Moor Street to Bicester North Station. There is a direct bus link from the station to Bicester Village.

Top 30

Agent Provocateur ★ ★ ★ ★
Telephone: 01869 250762
Since 1994, Agent Provocateur has been producing its racy lingerie and accessories at discounts of between 30% and 50%. Most of the products here are end-of-line. They also have an online sale. This is their only outlet shop.

Anya Hindmarch ✦✦✦✦
Telephone: 01869 247963
A good selection of past seasons' handbags along with accessories at discounts of up to 40% off the London boutique shop prices and even better deals on past seasons' collections.

Bonpoint ✦✦✦✦
Telephone: 01869 248433
Bonpoint's 6 London shops send previous seasons' children's wear to their outlet at Bicester at discounts starting at 30%, with a selection of clothing, shoes and accessories for boys, girls and newborns.

Books Etc ✦✦✦✦
Telephone: 01869 325417
Books Etc is part of Borders and has a good selection of coffee table books, fiction and non-fiction along with travel guides. Discounts start at 30% and rise to as much as 80%.

Camper ✦✦✦
Telephone: 01869 324460
This casual Spanish shoe company has its only outlet here, selling its quality end of seasons' stock at discounts of between 35% and 50%, along with seasonal promotions.

Cath Kidston ✦✦✦
Telephone: 01869 327222
Cath Kidston's kitsch style has achieved iconic status worldwide, and here she sells seconds and the last couple of seasons' stock at discounted prices.

Celine ✦✦✦✦
Telephone: 01869 360639
This Paris designer's outlet shop has a selection of ready to wear clothing, along with handbags, purses and silk scarves with discounts of 33%.

Dior ✦✦✦✦
Telephone: 01869 357725
The boutique offers last seasons' fashions at up to 80% off, with a good selection of clothes, shoes and accessories and includes a small section for men.

Dolce & Gabbana
Telephone:
At the time of going to press this information was not available as the shop had not yet opened.
Please telephone the Bicester Village information line on 01869 323200 for more information.

Dunhill ★ ★ ★
Telephone: 01869 354950
This smart gentleman's retailer offers discounts of 40% and over on last seasons' formal and causal collections. It also has a great end of season sale.

Folli Follie ★ ★ ★
Telephone: 01869 243644
Great reductions can be found at the only UK outlet, selling end-of-line and last seasons' watches and jewellery at a 30% to 70% discount.

Gerard Darel
Telephone:
At the time of going to press this information was not available as the shop had not yet opened.
Please telephone the Bicester Village information line on 01869 323200 for more information.

Gieves and Hawkes ★ ★ ★ ★
Telephone: 01869 243711
This gentleman's outfitter has a great selection of formal shirts along with accessories, some suits and leather goods at discounts starting at 30%.

Jimmy Choo ★ ★ ★ ★
Telephone: 01869 247319
Any serious shoe shopper should head to Jimmy Choo's only UK outlet for amazing women's shoes at 40% and 60% below RRP.

Links of London ★ ★ ★ ★
Telephone: 01869 245534
Links, whose packaging stands out above the rest, sell their signature silver gifts and jewellery at great discounts, along with some special purchases. All items can be gift wrapped with Links' fantastic packaging.

Loro Piana ★ ★ ★ ★
Telephone: 01869 2255690
This luxury clothing brand opened its first UK outlet about 2 years ago at Bicester, with last seasons' merchandise at 50% off the RRP. There is a selection of fantastic buys at up to 70% off to be found at the back of the store. Beware, once you have felt the quality of their merchandise, nothing else will do!

Luella

Telephone:

At the time of going to press this information was not available as the shop had not yet opened. Please telephone the Bicester Village information line on 01869 323200 for more information.

Matthew Williamson

Telephone:

At the time of going to press this information was not available as the shop had not yet opened. Please telephone the Bicester Village information line on 01869 323 200 for more information.

Miss Sixty/Energie ★★★

Telephone: 01869 354601

This hip outlet has a good selection of women's and children's clothing at discounts starting at 40%. You can find some menswear under the Energie label.

Nicole Farhi ★★★

Telephone: 01869 252346

Both men's and women's collections are available with discounts of up to 30% on recent stock and up to 80% on older stock.

Ozwald Boateng ★★★★

Telephone: 01869 375125

This Savile Row tailor's only outlet shop sells previous men's suits and collections along with shoes at 30% off, rising to 80% during the sale period.

Salvatore Ferragamo ★★★★

Telephone: 01869 325373

The Italian leather company's only UK outlet carries leather goods, accessories and shoes for men and women with discounts up to 75%.

TAG Heuer ★★★★

Telephone: 01869 249008

This luxury watch brand has its only outlet here offering shop-soiled watches along with previous seasons' end-of-line stock at discounts of up to 50%.

Temperley London ★★★

Telephone: 01869 327143

The past seasons' bags and fashion collections from Alice Temperley can be found at discounts from 40% to 80%, along with some accessories.

The White Company ★★★★
Telephone: 01869 253393
A good selection of linens, clothing and home accessories can found at the outlet store. Discounts begin at 30%.

Tod's ★★★★
Telephone: 01869 325147
Tod's and Hogan share this outlet with a great range of shoes for both men and women, along with a full range of handbags and small leather goods. Discounts start at 40% with special offers giving up to an additional 40% off.

TSE ★★★
Telephone: 01869 244030
Previous seasons' men's and women's ready to wear collections are discounted by 50% with an additional discount of 20% on public holidays. TSE is also at Kildare in Ireland.

Tumi ★★★
Telephone: 01869 250553
This quality luggage manufacturer offers discounts on past ranges starting at 35%, with extra savings at certain times of the year.

Versace ★★★★
Telephone: 01869 252511
Men's and women's fashion and accessories are offered at discounts of up to 60%, at Versace's only UK outlet.

Wolford ★★★★
Telephone: 01869 357804
High-end hosiery and lingerie retailer Wolford have the previous year's collections at discounts of up to 75% off the retail price.

Also here:

Accessorize
All Saints
Anne Fontaine
Aquascutum
Bally
Bodum
Bose
Burberry
Café Coton
Calvin Klein

Calvin Klein Underwear
Cerruti 1881 Menswear
Charles Tyrwhitt
Church's English Shoes
Clarks
Coast
David Clulow
Descamps
Diesel
DKNY
Ermenegildo Zegna
Fat Face
Feraud Homme
Fred Perry
French Connection
Furla
Hackett
Helly Hansen
Hobbs
Hugo Boss
Jack Wills
Jaeger
Jigsaw
Karen Millen
Kenneth Turner
Kipling
LK Bennett
Levi's
L'Occitane
MaxMara
Mexx
Molton Brown
Monsoon
Mulberry
Musto
Myla
Nitya
N Peal
Onieda
Pascal Jewellery
Paul Smith
Petit Bateau
Penhaligon's

Polo Ralph Lauren
Pringle of Scotland
Puma
Quiksilver
Racing Green
Radley
Ralph Lauren Boys & Girls
Reebok
Reiss
Rock Couture
Samsonite
Savoy Taylors Guild
Studio Moda
Sunglass Time
Ted Baker
The Cosmetics Company Shop
The North Face
Theory
Thomas Pink
Timberland
Tog 24
Tommy Hilfiger
Vans
Vilebrequin
Villeroy & Bach
Waterford Wedgwood
Whistles

2. York Designer Outlet

St. Nicholas Avenue, Fulford, York, YO19 4TA,
Telephone: 01904 682700
www.yorkdesigneroutlet.com

Opening Hours:
Mon-Fri 10-6
Thurs 10-8
Sat 10-6
Sun 10*-5
*Larger shops open at 11
Bank Holidays 10-6

104 stores.

Top 10

Adidas ★ ★ ★
Telephone: 01904 655811
A good selection of past seasons' footwear and performance footwear, alongside clothing and football team shirts. Discounts start at 30% going up to 50%.

Armani/DKNY/Luella ★ ★ ★ ★
Telephone: 01904 679200
Various Armani collections, Luella handbags, ready-to-wear, and DKNY jeans. Discounts start at 40%.

Coast ★ ★ ★
Telephone: 01904 640743
The outlet has collections from some 50 stores and has discounts starting at 30%, but can go as high as 75% off the original selling price.

Daks ★ ★ ★ ★
Telephone: 01904 461040
Daks' only UK sale shop offers fantastic discounts of up to 80% off men's and women's collections and accessories. They also offer a mailing list to keep you informed of sales and offers.

Descamps ★ ★ ★ ★
Telephone: 01904 678607
This luxury French bathroom and bedroom label has a good selection of bed linens along with towels and accessories at discounts of up to 75% off last seasons' stock. Some seconds are also available.

Hackett ★ ★ ★ ★
Telephone: 01904 673799
An average of 30% discount can be found on previous seasons' menswear and boys' clothing. Extra discounts are found on promotional weekends.

Margaret Howell ★ ★ ★ ★
Telephone: 01904 634607
Top fashion designer Margaret Howell sells her previous collections at between 50% and 70% off. End of season sales can see reductions of up to 90%.

Penhaligons ★ ★ ★
Telephone: 01904 679151
This classic English perfumer has a good selection of fragrances, toiletries and some gifts at discounts of 50% and more. The perfumes aren't packaged in boxes.

Reebok ★ ★ ★
Telephone: 01904 613658
Last seasons' sports clothing along with sporting footwear is offered at discounts of 30% off the RRP. Additional discounts of a further 30% at sale times.

Timberland ★ ★ ★
Telephone: 01904 620333
This outdoor outfitter sells men's, women's and children's footwear and apparel, alongside luggage and accessories, at discounts of 30% and above.

Also Here:

Antler
Austin Reed
Autonomy
Bedeck
Ben Sherman

Bench & Hooch
Billy and Gruff Cashmere & More
Birthdays
Body Shop Depot
Bookends
Bose
Burberry
Cadbury Factory Shop
Calvin Klein Jeans
Calvin Klein Underwear
Chapelle
Charcoal & Chalk
Chilli Pepper
China China
Christy Outlet Store
Clarks Factory Outlet
Claire's Accessories
Coccinelle
Cotton Traders
Crew
Daniel Footwear
Denby
Designer Room
Designer Kidz
Dilemma Artwork
Donnay
Double Two
Famous Footwear
Fox Racing
Fred Perry
French Connection
Gap Outlet
Haggar
Hamleys Outlet
Hobbs
Home Curtains & Bedding
Hugo Boss
Intimas Lingerie
Jacques Vert Group
Jaeger
Jeff Banks Studio Store
Joules
Julian Graves

Karen Millen
KIDS
Klass
Lacoste
Le Creuset
Levi's
LK Bennett
Logo
Marks & Spencer Outlet
Mexx
Mooche
Mountain Warehouse
Moss/ Moss Bros Hire
Next Clearance
Nitya
O2
Oakley Vault
Olsen
Oneida
Paul Smith
Pavers Outlet
Perfume Point
Petroleum
Polo Ralph Lauren
Prima Designer Clothing
Professional Cookware
Racing Green
Ravel
Remington
Rockport
Roman Originals
Rugs Plus
Sand
Shoe Studio
Soft Shoe Company
Staccato Fashion Footwear
Suits You/ Young's Hire
Sunglass Time
Ted Baker
Tefal
Thomas Pink
The Paper Mill Shop
The Designer Studio

Tog 24
Tommy Hilfiger
Travel Accessory
Van Heusen
Vecopri
Virgin Cosmetics Company store
Viyella
Whittard Outlet
Wolsey
Zavvi

3. Cheshire Oaks

Management Suite, Kinsey Road, Ellesmere Port, South Wirral, CH65 9JJ
Telephone 0151 348 5600
www.cheshireoaksdesigneroutlet.com

Opening Hours:
Mon-Fri 10-8
Sat 10-7
Sun 10*-5
*Larger shops open at 11
Bank Holidays 10-6 (excluding Christmas Day)

127 stores

Top 10

Billabong ★ ★ ★
Telephone: 0151 3557722
Since 1973 Billabong has been producing its surf inspired clothing.
It can now be purchased here at 30% off the RRP, and up to 50% off during promotions.

Bose ★ ★
Telephone: 0151 3578300
Bose sells reconditioned sound systems and speakers at its outlet, all at a discounted prices. It also stocks its famous range of noise cancelling headphones, which are not discounted.

Charles Tyrwhitt Shirts ★ ★ ★
Telephone: 0151 3554647
Here you can find men's shirts, ties, shoes and suits at good discounts, along with a small selection of shirts for women.

Early Learning Centre ★ ★ ★
Telephone: 0151 3569474

The outlet sells toys (which are mostly end-of-line stock) and sale items at reductions starting at 30% off.

Kurt Geiger ★ ★ ★
Telephone: 0151 3550195
This high-end women's shoe retailer carries last seasons' and end-of-line stock, plus some seconds, at discounts of up to 75%.

Le Creuset – Denby ★ ★ ★
Telephone: 0151 3568385
These two companies have teamed up to sell old stock and some seconds, (all of which still have a guarantee) with discounts starting at 30% and going up to 50%.

Molton Brown ★ ★ ★ ★
Telephone: 0151 3571484
Most of the bath and body items, alongside travel and candle products, are reduced by up to 30% off the high street price.

Nike Factory Shop ★ ★ ★
Telephone: 0151 3571252
Sporting footwear and accessories can be found at discounts of up to 50%, with additional savings during sale periods.

Tommy Hilfiger ★ ★ ★
Telephone: 0151 3554501
This American outfitter has both men's and women's past seasons', which start at 33% off. Clearance items carry bigger discounts.

Villeroy and Boch ★ ★ ★
Telephone: 0151 355 7771
The German ceramics manufacturer has a number of outlets selling its current collections' seconds along with discontinued items. These are sold here at varying discounts.

Also here:

3 Mobile
Adidas
All Saints
Animal
Antler
Austin Reed
Autonomy

Baronjon
Bedeck
Bench & Hooch
Ben Sherman
Blue Inc
Brand Fusion
Burberry
Cadbury Factory Shop
Calvin Klein Jeans
Calvin Klein Underwear
Carphone Warehouse
Chapell Jewellery
Christy Outlet Store
Claire's Accessories
Clarks Factory Outlet
Cross
Coast
Cotton Traders
D2
Daniel Footwear
Designer Kidz Store
Designer Room
Diesel
Donnay
Dune
East
Ecco
Fat Face
Fiorelli
Fred Perry
Gap outlet
Goldsmith's Outlet
Jaeger
Jeff Banks Studio Store
Julian Graves
Karen Millen
Kitch' n 'Sync
Kurt Muller
Lacoste
La Senza

Lakeland
Lee Cooper
Levi's
Lilley & Skinner
Logo
Marks & Spencer Outlet
(menswear)
Marks & Spencer Outlet
(womenswear)
Mexx
Monsoon
Moss Bros
Mountain Warehouse
Mulberry
Next Clearance
Nitya
Oasis
Oneida
Perfume Point
Petroleum
Phase Eight
Pilgrim
Playtex/ Gossard/ Wonderbra
Playtime Toys
Polo Ralph Lauren
Ponden Mill
Prima Designer Men
Prima Tessuti
Pringle of Scotland
Professional Cookware
Puma
Pumpkin Patch
Racing Green
Reebok/ Rockport
Regatta
Remington
Revlon
Roman Originals
Royal Worcester
Samsonite Company Store

Sketchers
Soled Out
Sony
Suits You/ Young's Hire
Sunglass Time
Ted Baker
The Cosmetic Company Store
The North face
The Paper Mill shop
The Works
Timberland
TM Lewin
Tog 24
Toshiba
Tripp
Triumph
Tula
Vans
Virgin Cosmetic Company Store
Warehouse
Wedgwood
WH Smith

4. Ashford

Kimberley Way, Ashford, Kent, TN24 OSD
Telephone: 01233 895900
www.ashforddesigneroutlet.com

Opening Hours:
Mon-Fri 10-8
Sat 10-7
Sun 10*-5.
*Larger shops open at 11
Bank Holidays 10-6 (excluding Christmas Day)

Top 10

Bench and Hooch ★ ★ ★
Telephone: 01233 625625
This urban lifestyle brand (based on its skateboard heritage) offers men's and women's apparel and accessories at discounts of up to 75%.

Benetton ★ ★ ★
Telephone: 01233 625684
Men's and women's fashions from previous seasons sit alongside samples. Reductions of up to 70%. (Also at Clarks Outlet Village, Somerset.)

Ecco ★ ★ ★
Telephone: 01233 626020
Footwear for the entire family can be found here with discounts starting at 30% for previous seasons' collections.

Fat Face ★ ★ ★
Telephone: 01233 638616
Men's, women's and children's clothing can be found at discounts of up to 70% from this casual brand.

Goldsmiths ★ ★ ★
Telephone: 01233 612233
Goldsmiths has 5 outlets selling its jewellery, end-of-line and discontinued items at discounts of between 50% and 70%.

Kipling ★★★
Telephone: 01233 626897
This casual travel bag company offers last seasons' bags and luggage at a minimum discount of 30%.

Polo Ralph Lauren ★★★
Telephone: 01233 895080
Past seasons' collections for men, women and children are available at discounts of up to 60% off the RRP, with further reductions at sale times.

Professional Cookware ★★★
Telephone: 01233 624126
This kitchen shop stocks a large selection of high-end kitchenalia at good prices. Items on clearance have good discounts.

Revlon ★★★★
Telephone: 01233 645421
This outlet sells Revlon's past collections and limited editions of make-up and fragrance. Discounts start at 30%.

TM Lewin ★★★★
Telephone: 01233 665675
This Savile Row tailor's outlet sells both formal and casual shirts and suits for both men and women with great discounts. You can use your loyalty card here, too.

Also here:

Adidas
Animal
Antler
Autonomy
Baronjon
Ben Sherman
Bookends
Bose
Calvin Klein Underwear
Carphone Warehouse
Chapelle Jewellery
China Place
Christy Outlet Store
Claire's Outlet

Clarks Factory Outlet
Collector's Store
Cotton Traders
Denby
Design House
Designer Kids
Designer Room
Donnay
Ecco
Fred Perry
Gap Outlet
Henri Lloyd
Jeff Banks Studio Store
Kurt Geiger
Lacoste
Levi's
Lilley & Skinner
Logo
Marks & Spencer Outlet
Mexx
Moss/Moss Bros Hire
Mountain Warehouse
Next Clearance
Nike Factory Store
Oasis
The Paper Mill Shop
Perfume Point
Phase Eight
Playtex/ Gossard/ Wonder Bra
Principles
Puma
Racing Green
Reebok
Roman Originals
Samsonite Company Stores
Soled Out
Staccato
Suits You/ Young's Hire
Ted Baker

Tog 24
Tommy Hilfiger
Toshiba
Tula
Van Heusen
Whittard
Zavvi

5. Gunwharf Quays

Gunwharf Quays
Portsmouth, Hampshire, PO1 3TZ
Telephone: 02392 836700
www.gunwharf-quays.com

Opening Hours:
Mon-Fri 10-7
Sat 9-7
Sun 10*-5
*larger shops open at 11

Top 10

Banana Republic ★ ★ ★ ★
Telephone: 02392 755493
The UK's only Banana Republic outlet sells its preppy and crisp last seasons' collection for men, women and children. Discounts at up to 60%.

Dune ★ ★ ★
Telephone: 02392 753674
Men's and women's stylish shoes can be found at this outlet, with discounts averaging 45%.

Ghost ★ ★ ★
Telephone: 02392 291681
The quality women's wear collections are reduced by up to 70% here.

Hobbs ★ ★ ★
Telephone: 02392 739238
This high-end high street chain sells past seasons' womenswear and footwear at discounts starting at 30%.

Jack Wills ★ ★ ★ ★
Telephone: 02392 817912
This university, preppy brand sells its previous seasons' collections at discounts of between 30% and 50%.

Kenneth Turner ★ ★ ★ ★
Telephone: 023 92 818132
The two outlets at Gunwharf and Bicester sell past seasons' collections of home accessories and candles at discounts starting at 50%.

Liz Claiborne ★ ★ ★
Telephone: 02392 816393
This American quality ladies clothing and accessories line is offered here at 30% to 50% off RRP.

L'Occitane ★ ★ ★
Telephone: 02392 739021
You can't find the best sellers in this outlet, but they have great discounts on gift sets and mix and match products at discounts of up to 50%.

Oakley ★ ★ ★
Telephone: 02392 296720
Famous for sunglasses but also selling performance footwear, clothing and accessories with discounts up to 50%.

Paperchase ★ ★ ★ ★
Telephone: 02392 873262
A good selection of Paperchase's old stock can be found at great discounts; as much as 75% off the high street stores' prices.

Also Here:

Adidas
Animal
Antler
Austin Reed
Bags Etc
Barbour
Bedeck
Bench & Hooch
Boots
Bose
Burberry
Cadbury
Carphone Warehouse
Chapelle
Christy
Calvin Klein Underwear
Claire's Accessories

Clarks Factory Outlet
Clinton Cards
Cotton Traders
Crabtree & Evelyn
Crew Clothing Co.
Daniel James Jewellers
Denby & Le Creuset
Donnay International
ECCO
Fat Face
Fred Perry
French connection
Gap
Guess
Gul International
HMV
Julian Graves
Karen Millen Whistles
Kipling
Lakeland Leather
Lee Cooper
Levi Strauss
LK Bennet
Mambo
Marks & Spencer Outlet
Mexx
Monsoon
Molton Brown
Mountain Warehouse
Next Clearance
Nike
Oasis
O'Neill
Oneida
Paul Smith
Polo Ralph Lauren
Puma
Reef
Remington
Rip curl
Savoy Taylors Guild and Hugo Boss
Suits You/Young's Hire
Sunglass Time

Ted Baker
That Great Food Place
The Cosmetics Company Store
The Gadget Company UK
The Paper Mill Store
The Perfume Shop
The Professional Cookware Company
The Works
Thornton's
Timberland
TM Lewin
Tog 24
Trade Secret Hairdressers and Shop
Tula
Vans
Villeroy & Boch
White Stuff
Whittard of Chelsea
William Hill
Wonderbra
Zavvi

6. Swindon Designer Outlet

Kemble Drive, Swindon, Wiltshire, SN2 2DY
Telephone 01793 507600
www.swindondesigneroutlet.com

Opening hours:
Mon-Fri 10-8
Sat 10-7
Sun 10*-5
*larger shops open at 11
Bank Holidays 10-6 (Closed Christmas Day)

73 stores

Top 10

Austin Reed ★ ★ ★
Telephone: 01793 484424
High street tailoring for both men and women is available from past seasons' stock. You can also get seconds in both formal and casual lines at discounts starting at 33% and rising.

Evisu/Stone Island ★ ★ ★
Telephone: 01793 529170
This is the only outlet selling clothing for men, women and children, including a selection of shoes (formal and casual) at discounts of between 30% and 50%.

Gap Outlet ★ ★
Telephone: 01793 486696
Gap has 11 outlets in the UK, selling its previous season's clothing for men, women and children at varying discounts.

Hamleys ★ ★ ★ ★
Telephone: 01793 538500
The famous London toyshop has two outlets: here and at York, which sell end-of-line toys and games at discounts of between 50% and 70%.

John Lewis ★ ★ ★ ★
Telephone: 01793 512454
This is John Lewis' first outlet, and sells a wide range of slight damaged white kitchen goods along with furniture and other end-of-line items at discounts of up to 50%.

Musto ★ ★ ★
Telephone: 01793 423023
Performance clothing for the sailing crowd can be found here, with discounts of up to 60% for both men's and womenswear.

Phase Eight ★ ★ ★
Telephone: 01793 614399
This outlet sells previous seasons' women's collections at discounts of up to 30% off the high street shops.

Tefal/Rowenta/Moulinex/Krups ★ ★ ★
Telephone: 01793 485637
Great deals on the above brands with a large selection of small, home electrical goods. Discounts of up to 60% off discontinued lines.

Shoon ★ ★ ★ ★
Telephone: 01793 422240
This performance shoe company has a good selection of men's, women's and children's discontinued and slightly damaged footwear at discounts of up to 30%

Thomas Pink ★ ★ ★
Telephone: 01793 431818
This quality shirt and accessories designer has a good selection of past seasons' stock reduced by 30% and increasing to as much as 75%. Join the mailing list to keep updated on sales and offers.

Also Here:

Alexon
Antler
Aquascutum
Artigiano
Autonomy
Ben Sherman
Billabong
Burberry
Cadbury Factory Shop
Calvin Klein Underwear

Carphone Warehouse
Chapelle
Charles Tyrwhitt
Christy Home Outlet Store
Claire's Accessories
Clarks Factory Outlet
Cotton Traders
Crew Clothing Co
Denby
Donnay
Doulton and Company
Emporio Home
Foot Looker
Goldsmith's
Green and Pleasant
Henri Lloyd
Hi-Tec
Hobbs
Home Curtains & Bedding
Hugo Boss
Jaeger
Jane Shilton
Julian Graves
Klass Collection
Lakeland
Le Creuset
Levi's
Lilley & Skinner
LK Bennett
Marks & Spencer Outlet
Moss/Moss Bros Hire
Mountain Warehouse
Next Clearance
Nike Factory Outlet
Olsen
Petroleum
Polo Ralph Lauren
Ponden Mill
Portmeirion
Professional Cookware
Puma
Pumpkin Patch
Quiksilver

Regatta
Samsonite Company Stores
Suits You/Young's Hire
Sunglass Time
Ted Baker
The Luxury Beauty
The Paper Mill Shop
The Works Outlet
Thorntons
Timberland
Tog 24
Toyzone
Tommy Hilfiger
Tula
Tutta Bella, Nails and Beauty
Waterford Wedgewood
Whittard of Chelsea
World Belts
Van Heusen
Yankee Candle
Zavvi

7. Clarks Village

Farm Road, Street, Somerset, BA16 OBB
Telephone: 01458 840064
www.clarksvillage.co.uk

Opening Hours:
Mon-Sat 9-6
Sun 10-5
Late night shopping every Thursday til 8

Top 10

Calvin Klein ★ ★ ★
Telephone: 01458 840557
The outlet sells pyjamas, underwear and swimwear for both men and women at up to 50% discount.

Crabtree & Evelyn ★ ★ ★
Telephone: 01458 841440
Discontinued lines for bathroom, bedroom, kitchen and garden are available here with discounts starting at 10%.

Gaggia ★ ★ ★ ★
Telephone: 01458 447025
Discounts of up to 56% can be found on espresso and cappuccino machines that failed to sell at the original price; all come with a two year guarantee.

Karen Millen ★ ★ ★
Telephone: 01458 448533
Karen Millen, the high street retailer, offers previous seasons' collections here, with discounts of between 30% and 70%.

Orvis ★ ★ ★ ★
Telephone: 01458 443805
This country sports outfitter has a good selection of clothing accessories and some fishing equipment at varying discounts.

Rohan ★ ★
Telephone: 01458 841849
The Rohan outlet sells end-of-line climate control clothing and travel accessories at up to 20% off RRP.

Savoy Taylors Guild ★ ★ ★
Telephone: 01458 443769
This gentleman's outfitters sells end of season collections at discounts of between 20% and 40%.

The Body Shop ★ ★ ★
Telephone: 01458 441952
The outlet carries a good selection of mainly discontinued lines; including toiletries, cosmetics and bathroom products. Discounts of up to 50%.

Van Heusen ★ ★ ★
Telephone: 01458 447233
End-of-line shirts, (both formal and casual) ties and accessories can be found at discounts of up to 50% off the high street prices.

White Stuff ★ ★ ★
Telephone: 01458 448789
The outlet sells last seasons' fashions at discounts of around 30%, with larger discounts at sale times.

Also Here:

Adidas
Alexon
Artigiano
Autonomy
Bags Etc
Bedeck
Billabong
Cadbury
Chapelle Jewellery
Christy
Claire's Accessories
Clarks
Clarks Baggage Factory
Clarks Full Price
Coast
Cotton Traders

Crew Clothing Co
Dartington Crystal
Denby Pottery Company Ltd
Double Two
ECCO
The Edinburgh Woolen Mill
Event Jewellery
Fat Face
GAP
Hallmark
Hawkshead
Henri Lloyd
Jaeger
Jane Shilton
Jeff Banks
Joules
Julian Graves
Lakeland Leather
La Senza
Le Creuset
Lillywhites
Marks & Spencer
Michael Copper's Studio
Monsoon
Mountain Warehouse
Next Clearance
Nike Factory Store
Oneida
The Paper Mill Shop
Past Times
The Perfume Shop
Ponden Mill
Portmeirion
Price's Candles
Prima Designer Clothing
ProCook
Roman Originals
Royal Worcester & Spode
Ruby and Roses
Saltrock
Sonex Presents Sony
Stone
Suits You

Sunglass Time
Thorntons
Timberland
Tog 24
Tor Stone
Trespass
Triumph
Tula
United Colours of Benetton
Vodafone
Waterford Wedgwood
Whittard of Chelsea
Windsmoor/Jacques Vert
The Works
Zavvi

Coppa Sliced
£2.80 per 100g

Manzo Tir
£3.70

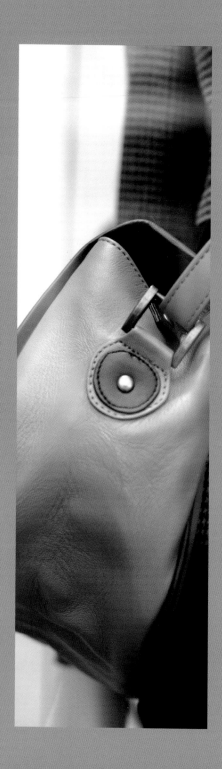

8. Livingston Designer Outlet

Almondvale Avenue, Livingston, West Lothian, EH54 6QX, Scotland
Telephone 01506 423600
www.livingstondesigneroutlet.com

Opening Hours:
Mon-Sat 9-6
Thurs 9-8
Sun 11-6

75 stores

Top 10

Autonomy ★ ★ ★
Telephone: 01506 400800
This women's outlet sells its past seasons' fashion collections at great discounts and also has special offers throughout the year.

Black and Decker ★ ★ ★
Telephone:01506 400948
The outlet sells excess stock of power tools and dust busters, along with some reconditioned items at discounts of up to 30% off the retail price.

Designer Kidz ★ ★ ★
Telephone: 01506 420632
This children's fashion clothing retailer sells its past seasons' stock at discounts starting at 50%, but can be as much as 75%.

DNKY/Armani ★ ★ ★ ★
Telephone: 01506 462194
The past seasons' men's and women's collection from both brands, along with some accessories, are sold at discounts of up to 50% off original collection prices.

Donnay ★ ★ ★
Telephone: 0870 3339534
This sportswear retailer sells excess stock and older styles at discounts of up to 70%, for men, women and children.

Kurt Muller ★ ★ ★
Telephone: 01506 418247
Selling previous seasons' collections for men and women, with discounts starting at 30%. There are frequent sales throughout the year that carry larger discounts.

Perfume Point ★ ★ ★
Telephone: 01506 461755
A great selection of perfumes and aftershaves are available at discounts starting at 50% off the original selling price.

Sunglass Time ★ ★ ★
Telephone:01506 461177
This outlet houses a large collection of top designers' models; including Oakley, Dior and Armani. Discounts of between 30% and 50%. Clearance items up to 70% off the retail price.

Ted Baker ★ ★ ★
Telephone: 01506 460882
Men's, women's and children's previous seasons' collections can be found with discounts starting at 30%.

Virgin Cosmetics ★ ★ ★
Telephone: 01506 463344
The outlets sell last year's old stock of make-up and beauty solutions at discounts of between 50% and 75%.

Also here:

Antler
Aquascutum
Bags Etc
Bedeck
Ben Sherman
Bench & Hooch
Brand-Fusion
Cadbury
Calvin Klein Jeans
Claire's Accessories
Chapelle Jewellery

Charles Clinkard
Christy Outlet Store
Clarks Factory Outlet
Cotton Traders
Cruise Clearance
Daniel Footwear
Denby
Designer room
Fat Face
Fred Perry
Gap Outlet
Gleneagles Crystal
Home & Cook
Julian Graves
Karen Millen
Klass
Le Creuset
Levi's
Lilley & Skinner
Logo for Less
Luxury Beauty Store
Marks & Spencer Outlet
Merchants fine Jewellery
Mexx
Moss/Moss Bros Hire
Next Clearance
Nitya
Oasis
Olsen
Outdoor Scene
Petroleum
Phones 4 U
Playtex/Gossard/Wonderbra
Professional Cookware
Reebok
Regatta
Revlon
Roman Originals
Rugs Plus
Select
Sketchers
Soled Out
Suits You/ Young's hire

The Designer Studio
The Paper Mill Shop
Tog 24
Trespass
Tula
Urban
Van Heusen
Whittard Outlet
Windsmoor
Zavvi

9. Freeport Braintree

Charter Way, Chapel Hill, Braintree, Essex, CM77 8YH
Telephone: 01376 348168
www.freeport-braintree.com

Opening Hours:
Mon-Fri 10-6
Sat 9-7
Sun 10-5
Late night shopping every Thursday til 8

Top 10

All Wellan Good ★ ★ ★
Telephone: 01376 567784
All 10 outlets around the country sell cosmetics, toiletries and perfumes at discounts of up to 70%.

Barbour ★ ★ ★
Telephone: 01376 553679
The outlet sells discontinued and quality approved seconds for men and women, along with outdoor clothing, at variable discounts.

Burberry ★ ★ ★
Telephone: 01376 554851
Along with the two factory shops, the outlet shop sells past seasons' collections; for men, women and children.

Christy Towels ★ ★
Telephone: 01376 553078
The outlet sells towels, bed linen and accessories at discounts starting at 50%.

D selling Diesel ★ ★ ★
Telephone: 01376 320990
Diesel's men's and women's clothing along with items from Miss Sixty and Energie can be found here with discounts from 50% to 75%.

Lacoste ★ ★ ★
Telephone: 01376 332128
The French casual clothing of Lacoste, for men, women and children, can be found here with discounts beginning at 30% and rising to 70%.

Mountain Warehouse ★ ★ ★
Telephone: 01376 349595
The outlet has a good selection of equipment and clothing for outdoor pursuits at discounts of up to 70%.

Racing Green ★ ★ ★
Telephone: 01376 349899
The menswear collection sells tailoring and casual wear with discounts starting at 30%.

Samsonite ★ ★ ★
Telephone: 01376 569241
Samsonite's quality luggage is made in Belgium and the outlet offers past collections with discounts of up to 70%.

Wedgwood ★ ★ ★
Telephone: 01376 326880
The outlet sells Wedgwood, Waterford and Johnson Brothers at discounts of up to 75%.

Also Here:

Antler
Austin Reed
Autonomy
Bags etc
Barbour Womenswear Clearance
Baron Jon
Bijoux
Billabong
BOSE
Brand Fusion
Cadbury
Camille
Chapelle Jewellery
Claire's Accessories
Clarks
Cotton Traders
Crew Clothing
Denby Pottery
Designer Room
Donnay
Double two
Fone Gadgets
Gaggia
Home Curtains & Bedding
Hush Puppies

Intimas
Jaeger
Julian Graves
Karen Millen
Klass
Kurt Muller
Lilley & Skinner
Lipsy Clothing
Marks & Spencer
Mexx
New Era Cap
Next Clearance
Nike
Orange
Past Times
Petroleum
Pilot
Ponden Mill
ProCook
Proudfoot
Reebok
Regatta
Roman Originals
Sasperilla
Savoy Taylors Guild
Soled Out
Specs & Lenses
Staccato
Stone
Suits You
Ted Baker
The Paper Mill Shop
The Perfume Shop
Tommy Hilfiger
Trespass
Tula
Van Heusen
Villeroy & Boch
Whittard of Chelsea
Wonderbra, Playtex and Shock Absorber
Zavvi

10. Whiteley Village

Whiteley Way, Whiteley, Fareham, Hants, PO15 7LJ
Telephone: 01489 886886

Opening Hours:
Mon-Sat 10-6
Sun 11-5

Top 10

Easyliving Furniture ★★
Telephone: 01489 588355
Good discounts can be found on sofas, dining and bedroom furniture with discounts starting at 25%, with larger discounts and promotions during the year.

Emma Somerset ★★★★
Telephone: 01489 559944
The previous seasons' collections, along with hats, belts and shoes, with discounts starting at 30%.

High and Mighty ★★★★
Telephone: 01489 564616
The high-end retailer for big and tall men has a great selection of previous collections of up to 50% off the RRP.

Joseph ★★★★
Telephone: 01489 580082
The men's and women's collections stand alongside collections from For All Mankind at varying discounts. (Along with a great sale!)

Lillywhites ★★★
Telephone: 08703 339615
The famous Piccadilly store sends end of season clothing and footwear to its Whiteley outlet and discounts start at 30%.

Past Times ★★★
Telephone: 01489 588535
This outlet has gifts, accessories, books and sale items from high street shops with discounts starting at 30%.

Price's Candles ★★
Telephone: 01489 565150
This candle manufacturer sells its entire range at up to 30% off RRP.

Top Table ★★★
Telephone: 01489 580258
Sells everything for your kitchen and dining room, including some small electrical appliances. Discounts start at 30%.

Trespass ★★★
Telephone: 01489 571040
Sells quality outdoor and ski clothing with discounts starting at 30%.

Whittards of Chelsea ★★
Telephone: 01489 582071
This shop sells packaged teas and coffees, also gift sets, teapots and mugs with various discounts.

Also Here:

Artigiano
Baggage Factory
Banana Books
Boswells
Camille Lingerie
Chapelle Jewellery
Chilli Pepper
Claire's Accessories
Clinton Cards
Cotton Traders
D2
Designer Room
Double Two
Fox Sport
Home Curtains & Bedding
Jaeger
Julian Graves
Klass
Lilley & Skinner
Madhouse
Mark Marengo Fashion

Moss
Outdoor Project
Pavers
Petroleum
Pilot
Ponden Mill
Robinson Reade
Roman Originals
Room
Samsonite
Select
The Paper Mill
Winchester Village Furniture

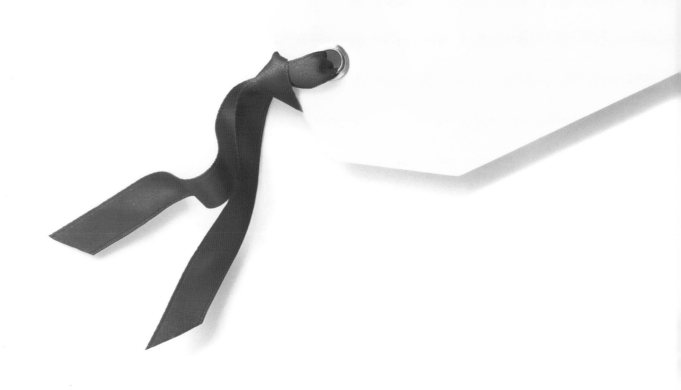

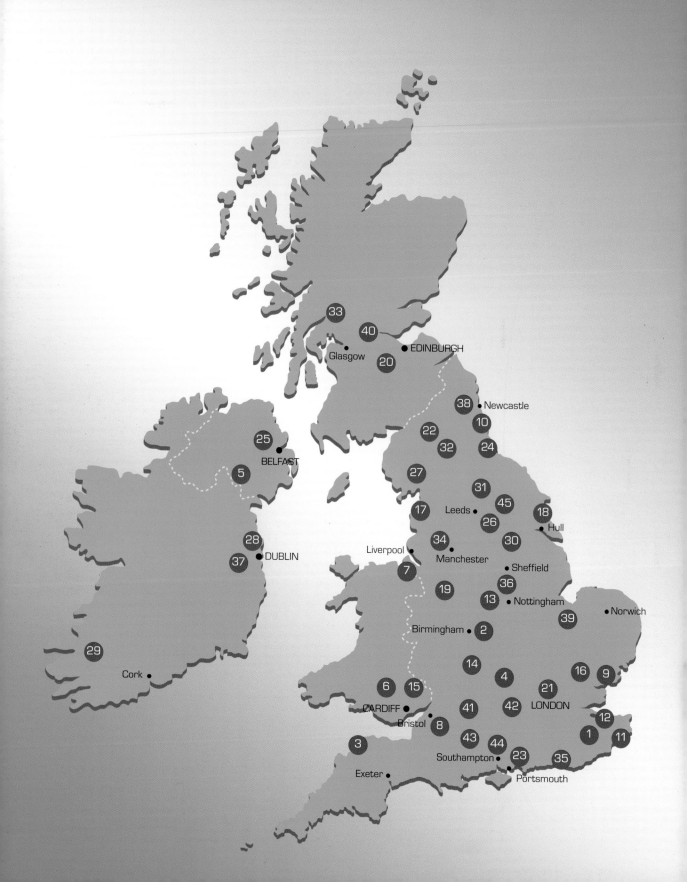

33

40

Glasgow • ● EDINBURGH

20

38 ● Newcastle

22 10

32 24

25

BELFAST

5

27

31

17 Leeds • 45 18

● 26 ● Hull

34

28

37 ● DUBLIN

Liverpool • 30

Manchester •

7

● Sheffield

19

36

13 ● Nottingham

39 ● Norwich

29

Birmingham • 2

14

16 9

4

Cork •

6 15

21 LONDON

CARDIFF •

41 42

8

12

Bristol •

43 44 1 11

3

23

35

Southampton •

Exeter •

Portsmouth

UK and Ireland Outlet Villages

1 Ashford

Kimberley Way, Ashford, Kent, TN24 OSD
Telephone: 01233 895900
Opening hours: Mon -Fri 10-8
Sat 10-7
Sunday 10*- 5
*Larger shops will open at 11
Bank Holidays - 10 to 6 (excluding Christmas Day)
www.ashforddesigneroutlet.com
Number of Stores: 75

2 Astle Outlet Park

West Bromwich, Birmingham, B70 8NS
Telephone: 01782 744113
Opening hours:
Mon-Sat 10-6
Thurs 10-8
Sunday 11-5
www.astlepark.co.uk
Number of Stores: 10

3 Atlantic Village Outlet

Clovelly Road, West of Bideford,
A39, North Devon, EX39 3QU
Telephone: 01237 422544
Opening hours:
Mon-Sat 10-6
Thurs 10-8
Sun10.30-4.30
Bank Holidays - 10-6
www.atlanticpark.co.uk
Number of Stores: 39

4

Bicester Village

50 Pingle Drive, Oxon, OX26 6WD
Telephone: 01869 323200
Opening hours:
Open late Mon-Sat 10-8
Sun 10-6
www.bicestervillage.com
Number of Stores: 130

5 Bridgend designer outlet

The Derwen, Bridgend, South Wales, CF32 9SU
Telephone: 01656 665700
Opening hours:
Mon-Fri 10-8
Sat 10-7
Sun 10-5
Bank Holidays 10-6
www.bridgenddesigneroutlet.com
Number of stores: 83

6 Bridgewater Park

Bridgewater Park, Banbridge, BT32 4GJ
Telephone: 028 4062 5151
Opening hours:
Mon-Wed 10-6
Thurs-Fri 10-9
Sat 9-6
Sun 1-6
www.the-outlet.co.uk
Number of stores: 61

7 Cheshire Oaks

Management Suite, Kinsey Road, Ellesmere Port, South Wirral, CH65 9JJ
Telephone +44 (0) 151 348 5600
Opening hours:
Mon-Fri 10-8
Sat 10-7
Sun 10*-5
*Larger shops will open at 11
Bank Holidays 10-6 (excluding Christmas Day)
www.cheshireoaksdesigneroutlet.com
Number of stores: 120

8 Clarks Village

Farm Road, Street, Somerset,
Telephone 01458 840 064
Opening hours:
Mon-Sat 9-6
Sun 10-5
Late night shopping every Thursday 'til 8
www.clarksvillage.co.uk
Number of stores: 85

9 Clacton Shopping Village
Stephenson Rd West, Clacton-On-Sea, Essex, CO15 4TL
Telephone: 01255 479595
Opening hours:
Mon-Sat 10-6
Sun 11-5
Bank Holidays 10-5
www.clactonvillage.co.uk
Number of stores: 24

10 Dalton Park
Murton, Co. Durham, SR7 9HU
Telephone: 0191 526 6157
Opening hours:
Mon-Fri 10-6
Thurs- Late night 8
Sat 9.30-6
Sun11-5
www.dalton-park.co.uk
Number of stores: 59

11 De Bradelei Wharf
Cambridge Road, Dover, Kent, CT17 9BY
Telephone: 01304 226616
Opening hours:
Mon-Fri 9.30-5.30
Sat 9.30-6
Sun & Bank Holidays 10.30-4.30
www.debradelei.com
Number of stores: 52

12 Dockside Factory Outlet
Maritime Way, Chatham Marina, Chatham, Kent, ME4 3ED
Telephone: 01634 899389
Opening hours:
Mon-Fri 10-6
Thurs10-8
Sat 10-6
Sun 11-5
www.docksideshopping.co.uk
Number of stores: 48

13 East Midlands Designer Outlet
Mansfield Road, South Normanton, Derbyshire, DE55 2JW
Telephone: 01775 545000
Opening hours:
Mon-Fri 10-6
Thurs 10-8
Sat 9.30-6.30
Sun 10-5
www.eastmidlandsdesigneroutlet.com
Number of stores: 61

14 Evesham Country Park
Eversham, Worcester, WR11 4TP
Telephone: 01386 41661
Opening hours:
Mon-Sat 9-6 (5.30 winter)
Sun 10.30-4.30
www.eveshamcountrypark.co.uk
Number of stores: 9

15 Festival Park
Victoria, Ebbw Vale, Gwent, NP23 8FP
Telephone: 01495 350010
Opening hours:
Mon-Sat 9.30-5.30
Sun 11-5
Thurs- Late night 7
www.festivalshopping.co.uk
Number of stores: 39

16 Freeport Braintree
Charter Way, Chapel Hill, Braintree, Essex, CM77 8YH
Telephone 01376 348 168
Opening hours:
Mon-Fri 10-6
Sat 9-7
Sun 10-5
Late night shopping every Thursday 'til 8
www.freeport-braintree.com
Number of stores: 85

17 Freeport Fleetwood

Anchorage Road, Fleetwood, Lancashire, FY7 6AE
Telephone: 01253 877377
Opening hours:
Mon-Sun 10-6
Thurs- Late night 8
www.freeport-fleetwood.com
Number of stores: 49

18 Freeport Hornsea

Rolston Road, East Yorkshire, HU18 1UT
Telephone: 01964 534211
Opening hours:
Mon-Sun 9.30-6
www.freeporthornsea.info
Number of stores: 28

19 Freeport Talke

Pit Lane, Stoke-On-Trent, Staffordshire, ST7 1XD
Telephone: 01782 744113
Opening hours:
Mon-Sat 10-6
Thurs 10-8
Sun 11-5
www.freeport-talke.com
Number of stores: 32

20 Freeport Leisure Village

Westwood, West Lothian, EH55 8QB
Telephone: 01501 763488
Opening hours: 10am 363 days a year
Number of stores: 5

21 Galleria Outlet Centre

Comet Way, Hatfield, Hertfordshire, AL10 0XR
Telephone: 01707 256860
Opening hours:
Mon-Fri 10-8
Sat 10-6
Sun 11-5
Bank Holidays 10-6
Number of stores: 76

22 Gretna Gateway Outlet Village
Glasgow Road, Gretna, DG16 5GG
Telephone: 01461 339100
Opening hours:
Mon-Sun 10-6
www.gretnagateway.com
Number of stores: 55

23 Gunwharf Quays
Portsmouth, Hampshire, PO1 3TZ
Telephone: 023 9283 6700
Opening hours:
Mon-Fri 10-7
Sat 9-7
Sun 10*- 5
*Due to Sunday trading law, larger stores are unable to open until 11
www.gunwharf-quays.com
Number of stores: 100

24 Jacksons Landing
The Highlight, Hartlepool Marina, TS24 0XN
Telephone: 01429 866989
Opening hours:
Mon-Sat 10-6,
Sun 11-5
www.shoppingvillages.com/jacksonlanding
Number of stores: 29

25 Junction 1
Antrim, BT41 4LL
Telephone: 028 9442 9111
Opening hours:
Mon-Wed 10-6
Thurs-Fri 10-9
Sat 9-6
Sun1-6
www.jnuctionone.co.uk
Number of stores: 70

26 Junction 32

M62, Castleford, West Yorkshire
Telephone: 01977 520153
Opening hours:
Mon-Fri 10-8,
Sat 10-6
Sun 11-5
www.Junction32.com
Number of stores: 84

27 K Village Outlet Centre

20 Strickland Gate, Kendal, LA9 4ND
Telephone: 01539 732 363
Opening hours:
Mon-Fri 9.30-6
Sat 9-6
Sun 10.30-4.30
Bank Holidays 9.30-6
www.kvillageoutletcentre.co.uk
Number of stores: 5

28 Kildare Village Outlet

Nurney Road, Kildare Town, County Kildare
Telephone: 353 (0) 45 520501
Opening hours:
Mon-Wed 10-6
Thurs 10-8
Fri-Sat 10-7
Sun 11-7
www.kildarevillage.com
Number of stores: 39

29 Killarney Outlet

Fair Hill, Killarney, Co. Kerry
Telephone: 353 (0) 64 36744
Opening hours:
Mon-Fri 10-7
Sat 10-6
Sun 12-6
Bank Holidays 12-6
www.killarneyoutletcentre.com
Number of stores: 23

30 Lakeside Village Outlet Shopping

White Rose Way, Doncaster
Telephone: 01302 366 444
Opening hours:
Mon-Fri 10-6
Thurs 10-8
Sat 9.30-6
Sun 10.30-5
www.lakeside-village.co.uk
Number of stores: 47

31 Lightwater Valley

North Stainley, Ripon, North Yorkshire, HG4 3HT
Telephone: 0871 720 0011
Opening hours: Call to check opening hours
www.lightwatervalley.co.uk
Number of stores: 9

32 Livingston Designer Outlet

Almondvale Avenue, Livingston, West Lothian, EH54 6QX, Scotland
Telephone +44 (0) 1506 423600
Opening hours:
Mon-Sat 9-6
Thurs 9-8
Sun 11-6m
www.livingstondesigneroutlet.com
Number of stores: 80

33 Loch Lomond

Alexandria, West Dumbartonshire, Scotland
Telephone: 01389 710077
Opening hours:
Mon-Fri 9.30-5.30
www.shoppingvillages.com/lochlomond
Number of stores: 19

34 Lowry

The Quays, Salford Quays, Manchester, M50 3AH
Telephone: 0161 848 1834
Opening hours:
Mon-Fri 10-6
Thurs 10-8
Sat 10-7
Sun 11-5
www.lowryoutletmall.com
Number of stores: 80

35 Merchants Quay

Telephone: 01273 818504
Brighton Marina Village, East Sussex, BN2 5UE
www.shoppingvillages.com/mechantsquay
Number of stores: 15

36 Peak Village Outlet Shopping

Chatsworth Road, Rowsley, Derbyshire, DE4 2JE
Telephone: 01629 735326
www.peakvillage.co.uk
Number of stores: 25

37 Rathdowney Shopping Outlet

Rathdowney, County Laois
Telephone: 353 (0) 505 48900
Opening hours:
Mon-Sat 10-6
Sun 11-6
www.rathdowneyoutlet.ie
Number of stores: 22

38 Royal Quays
Coble Dene, North Shields, NE29 6DW
Telephone: 0191 296 3743
Opening hours:
Mon-Fri 9.30-5.30
Sat 10.30-5
Thurs-Late night 8
www.royalquaysoutletcentre.co.uk
Number of stores: 48

39 Springfields Outlet Shopping
Camelgate, Spalding, Lincolnshire, PE12 6EU
Telephone: 01775 760 909
Opening hours:
Mon-Fri 10-6
Thurs-Late night 8
Sat 9-6
Sun 11-5
Bank Holidays 10-6
www.springfieldsshopping.co.uk
Number of stores: 54

40 Sterling Mills
Tillicoultry, Clackmannanshire, Scotland, FK13 6HQ
Telephone: 01259 752100
Opening hours:
Mon-Sat 10-6
Thurs Late night 7
Sun 11-6
www.sterlingmills.com
Number of stores: 45

41 Swindon Designer Outlet
Kemble Drive, Swindon, Wiltshire, SN2 2DY
Telephone +44 (0) 1793 507600
Opening hours:
Mon-Fri 10-8
Sat 10-7
Sun 10*- 5,
* larger stores opening at 11am
Bank Holidays - 10-6 (Closed Christmas Day)
www.swindondesigneroutlet.com
Number of store: 85

42 The Galleries

High Street, Aldershot, Hampshire, GU11 1PF
Telephone: 01252 341111
Opening hours:
Mon-Sat 9-6
Thurs-Late night 8
Sun- 11am-5pm
www.shoppingvillages.com/thegalleries
Number of stores: 19

43 The Wilton Shopping Village

Wilton, Salisbury, Wiltshire, SP2 0RS
Telephone: 01772 741211
Opening hours:
Mon-Sat 9.30-5.30
Sun 10.30-4.30
www.wiltonshoppingvillage.co.uk
Number of stores: 12

44 Whitley Village

Whitley Way, Whitley, Fareham, Hampshire, PO15 7LJ
Telephone: 01489 886886
Opening hours:
Mon-Sat 10-6
Sun 11-5
Bank holidays 10-5
www.whiteleyvillage.com
Number of stores: 46

45 York Designer Outlet

St. Nicholas Avenue, Fulford, York, YO19 4TA,
Telephone +44 (0) 1904 682700
Opening hours:
Mon- Fri 10-6
Thurs 10-8
Sat 10-6
Sun 10*-5
*Larger shops will open at 11
Bank Holidays 10-6
www.yorkdesigneroutlet.com
Number of stores: 120

Top 10 Sales

1. Harrods ★★★★★

87-135 Brompton Road, London, SW1X 7XL
Telephone: 0207 7301234
www.harrods.com
Winter Sale starts between 1st and 3rd January
Summer Sale starts last week of June (always on a Monday)

'There is only one Harrods Sale,' and with such an amazing collection of luxury goods, you can always find something at a great price. New sale merchandise is put out throughout the sale, and reductions of up to 90% can be found throughout the store's 300 plus departments. The first day of the sale always starts at 9am, and thereafter at 10am. Traditionally, there are always great buys in the clothing departments and the women's shoe sale is legendary. The furniture clearance room has a great selection of fine furniture, bedding and accessories. You can use your Harrods Reward card throughout the sale. You can also save an additional 10% on everything you purchase over specified weekends (normally two each sale period). Final reductions occur in the last week. This is when final clearance takes place also with massive reductions. It's easy to spend a day at the sale with the 29 eateries, and the spectacular food halls, so why not treat yourselves with all the money that you have saved. Send your purchased goods to Door 3 for collection. With new merchandise added daily, it is well worth visiting the Harrods Sale more than once. Remember, this is a very busy time, so try and plan your route around the store beforehand.

2. Johnston's of Elgin

New Mill, Elgin, Moray, IV30 4AF
Telephone: 01343 554099
www.johnstonscashmere.com
Sale starts in the last week of November (call for exact dates and times)
Opens to the public on the Saturday

This sale is worth getting on a plane for, which is why it ranks as our second best sale. Get a couple of friends and fly to either Inverness or Aberdeen, rent a car and take a big suitcase! A very large marquee is erected in the Mill's car park. Some 20,000 items are up for grabs here; you will find cashmere, other branded clothing and items for the home at fantastic prices. Johnston's manufacture for high-end speciality retailers around the world, and the seconds, overruns and samples are cleared in their sale. Upon arrival you are given a black sack instead of a basket, and can easily end up filling two sacks! We would suggest you make a weekend away of it and enjoy the beautiful scenery of the North East of Scotland.

3. Secret Sales

47-49 Park Royal Road, London, NW10 7LQ
Telephone: 0845 8739522
www.secretsales.com
customerservice@secretsales.com

Secret Sales is an online sale club, where membership is currently free. Their web-site offers an ever changing range of designer items of fashion, electronics, as well as items for the home. Each sale has a limited time span, but has large discounts of up to 80%. The company has excellent customer service, and a large customer base, so they must be doing something very well!

4. Hermes Sale

The Music Room, 26 South Moulton Lane, Mayfair, London, W1K 5AB
Telephone: 0207 4998856
www.hermes.com

Hermes has used a number of Mayfair locations in recent years and currently holds their sale in the Music Room on South Moulton Lane. Hermes can be quite fickle with their sales; sometimes they advertise, sometimes they don't. However, if you can find the 'when and where', there is a good selection of men's and women's ready-to-wear collections, along with shoes and accessories. The last couple of sales have also had wonderful porcelain collections. Discounts are either at 40% or 60%, and sometimes up to 80%. The quality is outstanding but, even with the discounts, expect to pay substantial amounts.

5. John Jenkins and Sons

Nyewood, Rogate, Nr Petersfield, Hampshire, GU31 5HZ
Telephone: 01730 821495
www.johnjenkins.co.uk
Sales in March, July and October (always starts on a Friday at 9:30)

John Jenkins is one of the country's leading crystal and glass manufacturers and has a 3000 sq ft warehouse shop. They hold three amazing sales throughout the year that include discounted lines, old stock and seconds; all are sold at very low prices to make way for their new lines. Many large items, usually only seen in high-end speciality stores, are discounted up to 80%. At sale times, almost everything in the shop is discounted. Join the mailing list to receive special offers and advance notification of sales.

6. The Great British Designer Sale

42 York Mansions, Prince of Wales Drive, London, SW11 4BP
Telephone: 0207 6272777
Email: bds@london83freeserve.co.uk

The original sample sale (celebrating 31 years of business) has four women's sales, two men's sales and one clearance sale a year at Chelsea Town Hall. You will find some 60 to 80 designers represented here, with discounts as much as 80%. BDS has a membership fee of £35.00 to gain access to the 3 days of sale previews, and the sale proper opens to the public on a Saturday with an entrance fee of £5.00. Apply for membership by phone, email or post.

7. Smythson

40 Bond Street, London, W1S 2DE
Telephone: 0207 3181515
www.smythson.com
Also at Sloane Street; Royal Exchange, Manchester
Concessions in Selfridges, Harrods, Harvey Nichols and Terminals 3 and 5 at Heathrow.

As one of the country's leading stationers, the stores have two short sales in January and July with a good selection of discontinued stock at discounts of up to 75%. A selection of leather goods can be found at the beginning of the sale at discounts of up to 80%. Get there early to get the best bargains.

8. Chelsea Textiles ★★★★

7 Walton Street, London, SW3 2JD
Telephone: 0207 7202200
Sale generally takes place in the first week of December at Chelsea Town Hall

This fantastic shop has the best soft furnishing sale we've found. A great selection of furniture, printed fabrics, cushions, accessories, (sometimes) crewel fabrics, and some ready-made special curtains; all at amazing prices! The best items are on day one and the sales normally last just a couple of days. Call to join the mailing list. We have the sale confirmed early this year, on the 12th, 13th, 14th and 15th November 2008.

9. Boden ★★★

Meridian West, Meridian Business Park, Leicester, LE19 1PX
Telephone: 0845 6775000
www.boden.co.uk

Boden runs its great online and mail order sales, as well as town hall sales across the country. They are all advertised locally, but if you are a Boden customer you will receive advanced notification of the sales. Discounts start at 40%. You can become a Boden customer by telephoning the number above, or by visiting the website.

10. Bicester Village Boxing Day Sale ★★★★

50 Pingle Drive, Bicester, Oxfordshire, OX26 6WD
Telephone: 01869 323200

If you need retail therapy after Christmas Day, Bicester Boxing Day Sale has some amazing bargains at its 130 stores when they clear out stock rooms and offer some fantastic bargains. The village is open from 10 to 7 on Bank Holidays.

Top 10 Sample Sales

1. London Fashion Weekend ★★★★★

Natural History Museum, Cromwell Road, London, SW7 5BD
Book tickets online or on the Ticket Hotline 0871 2301558
www.londonfashionweekend.co.uk
February and September

After London Fashion Week, the tents at The Natural History Museum are taken over by London Fashion Weekend. The five day event sees some 150 designers offer fabulous discounts on their clothes and accessories, with some late night openings until 9pm. Tickets start at £10.00 and go up to £15.50, with VIP passes priced at £75.00 (see website for details). The event has runway shows, attractions such as Toni and Guy's blowout salon, and a host of others; you will also find a champagne bar and, new for this year, a restaurant. It is a great day/evening out, which is why we give it the number 1 spot on this list.

2. Designer Warehouse Sales ★★★★★

5/6 Islington Studios, Thane Works, Thane Villas, London, N7 7NU
Telephone: 0207 837 3322
www.designerwarehousesales.com

An amazing collection of some 180 brands are stocked at the Designer Warehouse Sales at their new location at Islington Studios. DWS hold five women's sales and five men's sales per year, as well as some additional sales for exclusive brands. The items are from current collections, sample stock, one-off catwalk pieces and past seasons' collections. You may be here for several hours, so come prepared. Communal changing rooms are provided. Genuine discounts are between 60% and 80%. DWS celebrates its 21st birthday this year, and is has K Karl Lagerfeld and Hamish Marrow joining the sales this year. The entrance fee for all sales is £2.00.

3. London Accessory Sale ★★★★

Chelsea Town Hall SW11, Truman Brewery E1, and Notting Hill
info@londonaccessorysale.co.uk

These are the only dedicated accessories sales, and as many as 8 sales are held in a year at the three London locations. Join the mailing list to receive regular sale updates. The sales normally last just 4 hours and some 600 shoppers attended the last sale with items discounted up to 80%.

4. The Great British Designer Sale ★★★★

(also listed in Top 10 Sales)

42 York Mansions, Prince of Wales Drive, London, SW11 4BP
Telephone: 0207 6272777
Email: bds@london83freeserve.co.uk

The original sample sale (celebrating 31 years of business) has four women's sales, two men's sales and one clearance sale a year at Chelsea Town Hall. You will find some 60 to 80 designers represented here, with discounts as much as 80%. BDS has a membership fee of £35.00 to gain access to the 3 days of sale previews and the sales proper opens to the public on a Saturday with an entrance fee of £5.00. Apply for membership by phone, email or post.

5. Designer Sales UK ★★★

Straight Six Studios, Gibraltar Farm, Wick Street, Firle, Lewes, East Sussex, BN8 6NB
Telephone: 01273 858464
www.designersales.co.uk

Six sales are held throughout the year at the Truman Brewery on Brick Lane, London, E1, and some local sales in the Brighton and Lewes area. Over 100 designers are represented and many bargains are previewed on the catwalks at the sales. Discounts are between 60% and 90%. Join online to get advance notification and invites to preview days.

6. Lolapalooza ★★★

www.lolapalooza.co.uk

Julie Lewis' Lolapalooza sample sales are a much less stressful affair than other sample sales. The sales are at a number of London locations and travel into the West Country. They offer a great selection of designers along with some home collections at discounts of up to 70%. The sneak preview party means you get to shop a day early and enjoy champagne and canapés for £25.00. Limited tickets available. Apply on-line.

7. The Really Good Deal Fashion Sales ★★★

PO Box 75, Rochester, Kent, ME2 2DB
Telephone: 01367 860017
Ticket Hotline 01634 226203
www.ukgrandsales.co.uk
Sales in Ascot, Berkshire

Noelle Walsh's Really Good Deal Fashion Sales are in their 12th year with two sales in Ascot, in May and October. They offer products from 120 fashion companies, including all types of clothing and accessories, from bikini's to fur coats; all at fantastic discounts. Tickets cost £5.00 and can be booked via the ticket hotline or on the website.

8. Colefax and Fowler ★★★★

110 Fulham Road, London, SW3 6HU
Telephone: 0207 3737916
www.colefax.com

The Royal Horticultural Halls in Victoria house the once yearly sale of Jane Churchill, Colefax and Fowler, as well as a selection of Larson Fabrics (all available by the metre). Furniture, antiques, wallpaper and accessories are also on offer, at varying discounts off the retail price.

9. Secret Sample Sale ★★★

www.secretsamplesale.co.uk
mark@secretsamplesale.co.uk

The Sample Sale is made up of designers, agents and retailers who sell studio, showroom, catwalk and clearance stock at discounts of up to 80%. The sale is held in the Old Truman Brewery, London, E1. Dates and locations can be found on the website. Join the mailing list online to keep informed.

10. Billion Dollar Babes ★★★

Telephone: 0207 1934851
www.billiondollarbabes.co.uk

This American operation has started having sales in London and Dublin along with 5 US venues, selling the wares of 150 (mostly) American designers. Check the website for details of dates and times. There are membership programmes in place in the UK and US.

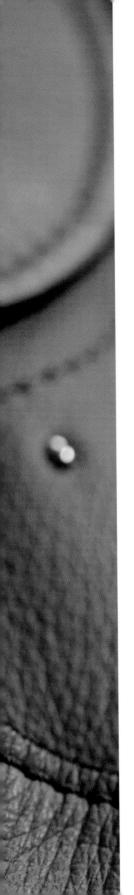

Top 10 Internet Sites
1. eBay ★★★★★
www.ebay.co.uk

Since it was founded in 1995, eBay, the online auction site, has become a worldwide household name, with approx. 82.3 million customers across some 39 markets. It's a global phenomenon. eBay has been active in the UK since 1999. The site makes its money by charging fees for listing items for its online auctions. It's interesting to note that during 2008, as the credit crunch takes hold, the number of listings for luxury brands has almost doubled.

eBay are spending millions every year tackling counterfeit merchandise and last year removed some 2.2 million counterfeit goods from the site. eBay always recommends paying by PayPal, its online payment system. As this book goes to press, eBay is raising the amount of cover it offers PayPal customers, from its current limit of £500 to £30,000.

2. Koodos ★★★★★

www.koodos.com

Koodos are a recent newcomer, launching in 2006 with their on-line private sales. This year, they were rated as one of the top 10 shopping internet sites in Retail Week and, consequently, Koodos are our second favourite online store. The site is free to join and you can select the private sales that you are interested in and receive email reminders. Koodos' by-line of 'be quick, be smart, be stylish' is easy to achieve with discounts of 40% to 80%.

3. Secret Sales ★★★★★

www.secretsales.com

(also listed in Top 10 Sales)

Secret Sales is an online sale club, where membership is currently free. Their web-site offers an ever changing range of designer items of fashion, electronics, as well as items for the home. Each sale has a limited time span, but has large discounts of up to 80%. The company has excellent customer service, and a large customer base, so they must be doing something very well!

4. Fashion Confidential ★★★★★

www.fashionconfidential.com

This website is the premier luxury fashion portal. The Fashion Confidential team scour the web each day to find what's hot and new in the fashion world, so its members never miss out. Members also receive exclusive VIP invitations to designer sample sales and sale previews. Fashion Confidential are highly regarded in the industry and have excellent relationships with many luxury brands.

5. Money Saving Expert ★★★★

www.moneysavingexpert.com
Martin Lewis's website offers expert advice and information on a host of consumer topics including shopping, finance, travel and other consumer related themes. You will also find discussion forums where you can share your opinions with other users about the issues the website raises. Martin is well known for his appearances on television and is a respected social commentator. The service is free.

6. Brand Alley ★★★★

www.brandalley.co.uk

The private sales at Brand Alley have discounts starting at 30% and going up to 70% off leading designers' clothes and accessories. The sales are short and sweet and the recommendation (as with all online private sales) is not to dither around too much as items tend to move very quickly. The site offers gift selections too, and expects to expand into the sporting goods market shortly.

7. Catwalk to Closet ★★★★

www.catwalktocloset.com

This London, internet based, sample sales company attracts worldwide attention and some 40,000 visitors a month. It has merchandise made up from press and buyer samples, alongside past collections from designers and boutiques. You can find great discounts here.

8. Net-a-Porter ★★★★

www.net-a-porter.com

This magazine style website offers up-to-the-minute fashion advice and online shopping sales for women, as well as a fashion advice hotline for its members. The website has a good mix of designers, is updated weekly and is viewed each month by 1.2 million women.

9. My Wardrobe ★★★

www.my-wardrobe.com

My Wardrobe is an online shopping boutique, which mainly sells at full price, but has a fabulous clearance sale with discounts of up to 75%. They offer mainly mid-priced designers' clothes but have some high-end collections, too.

10. Designermeout ★★★

www.designermeout.co.uk

This internet site has clothing and accessories for men and women from approximately 30 collections, ranging from Prada to True Religion Jeans. It was started in 2003.

Five More useful Websites

Daily Candy
www.dailycandy.com/london

Fashion Mag Daily
www.fashionmagdaily.com

Urban Junkies
www.urbanjunkies.com

Time Out Magazine
www.timeout.com/london

The Site Guide
www.thesiteguide.com

New York

The city that never sleeps offers its visitors world class shopping and the outlet shopping is second to none, catering for every budget. The city is easily navigated with excellent transport links, and the new Skytrain from JFK airport offers an affordable option for travel into Manhattan. New York's shops always seem to be having sales, and with the strong pound, it's bargains all round. A 50 minute ride up the 'thruway' takes you to the USA's premier outlet village, Woodbury Common. This massive village houses some 220 high quality outlets and offers a huge selection of discounted designer goods. Because many of the outlets here are only to be found at Woodbury, it's well worth the trek upstate. (It's obviously much easier to look here than to search through all the stock at the various discount retailers across Manhattan.) Do make sure you know what you want to shop for and leave enough time in which to find it. We suggest printing off the map and shop listings from the Woodbury Common website and planning your shopping en route from the city.

How to get there

Most of the airlines offer great fares to New York on their websites. If you already have a frequent flyer account with a specific airline, check that airline's website for prices (transatlantic flights soon clock up the air miles).

American Airlines - London to New York, including surcharges and tax, is approximately £320.

Before you travel

Checkout New York Magazine (www.nymag.com) sales and bargains sections on the website and Manhattan Users Guide (www.manhattanusersguide.com) for the following week's sales in the city.

Where to Stay

Larchmont Hotel
27 W. 11th Street, New York, NY 10011
Telephone +1 212 9899333
This small, friendly hotel is in a great central location on a tree-lined street between 5th and 6th Avenues, and close to transport links. The rooms are basic and prices start from $80 for a single and $109 for a double on weekdays, and from $99 for a single and $119 for a double at weekends.

W Hotels
www.starwoodhotels.com/whotels
The W Hotels are part of the Starwood Group. They are cool and modern with five locations across the city. Most have a 4 star rating. The best rates are available on-line and start at $190.00 per night plus taxes.

W New York – Lexington at 49th
Telephone +1 212 755 1200

W New York – Times Square
Telephone +1 212 930 7400

W New York – The Court
Telephone +1 212 685 1100

W New York – The Tuscany
Telephone +1 212 686 1600

W New York – Union Square
Telephone +1 212 253 9119

A Special Place to Stay:

Inn at Stony Creek
34 Spanktown Road, Warwick, New York, 10990
Telephone +1 (845) 986 3660
www.innatstonycreek.com

This beautiful Inn was built in 1840 and is set in 9 acres. It offers 5 guest rooms, the staff are very hospitable and it is situated just outside the town of Warwick. The Inn offers a morning drop off and evening collection from the Woodbury Outlets (round trip fee for $20). The rooms start at $99 - $235 per night.

Outlet Villages

Woodbury Common Premium Outlets
498 Red Apple Court, Central Valley, New York, 10917
Telephone +1 (845) 928 4000
www.premiumoutlets.com/woodburycommon

Opening Hours:
Mon-Sun 10-9

Woodbury Common is located just an hour away in upstate New York at junction 16 off the New York Thruway. It is by far America's best shopping mall, and houses the most exclusive designer collections and the largest number of one-off outlets in the US. The other 280 malls just don't compare. Can you do it justice in a day? Well, we have, but it really needs two or more days; its 220 outlet shops can be rather daunting (which is why we recommended a place to stay nearby where you will be pampered!). The mall has lockers that can be rented for $10 a day, so you can unload and squirrel away all your purchases til closing time. With 17 food outlets you won't go hungry, either. The best way to travel to Woodbury is on the Grayline bus from the Port Authority in Manhattan on 40th Street. The fare is $41.00 (round trip) and includes a VIP discount book that can give you extra discounts at many outlets, but does exclude many of the top designers. Collect your discount book from Woodbury's Information Tower in Red Apple Court. The website for Woodbury is very helpful and you can download store information and a location layout. Here we have reviewed 40 of the best outlets.

Top 40

Barney's New York +1 (845) 928 4455 ★ ★ ★
This large outlet has a good selection of past seasons' men's and womenswear along with some accessories and shoes at variable discounts. Barney's Warehouse Sale on 18th Street in Manhattan is worth visiting, too.

Betsey Johnson +1 (845) 928 4678 ★ ★ ★ ★
The whimsical and feminine designs of previous seasons' collections can be found at discounts from 30% to 60% off the boutique prices.

Bottega Venetta +1 (845) 928 4563 ★ ★ ★ ★
Past seasons' signature designs in luggage, handbags and small leather goods can be found here, along with some footwear for men and women. Discounts start at 30%.

Brunello Cucinelli Cashmere +1 (845) 928 5888 ★ ★ ★ ★ ★
This luxury Italian brand has just opened its first outlet shop in the USA and here you can find its signature clothing collections for men and women, along with some leather goods, at discounts of 40%.

Celine +1 (845) 928 5138 ★ ★ ★ ★
This Parisian label's outlet has women's ready-to-wear collections, along with handbags, shoes and some accessories, with discounts starting at 40%.

CH Carolina Herrera +1 (845) 928 0676 ★ ★ ★ ★
The outlet sells both men's and women's previous seasons' collections with accessories for women, including wallets, scarves and hats at discounts between 35% and 40%.

Chanel +1 (845) 928 1550 ★ ★ ★ ★ ★
This style icon brand has its only worldwide outlet here at Woodbury and offers its collections of past seasons' women's ready-to-wear, with a small selection for men. Discounts are at 60% off RRP (with handbags at 25% off). Costume jewellery and shoes are discounted between 25% and 40%.

Chloe +1 (845) 928 6260 ★ ★ ★ ★
Chloe's past seasons' collection of ready-to-wear is at 50% off the RRP. A selection of accessories and a limited selection of bags start at 35% off the boutique prices.

Converse +1 (845) 928 9978 ★ ★ ★
The famous basketball shoe manufacturer has just opened at Woodbury with discontinued shoes and casual clothing for men and women with discounts starting at 30%.

Diane Von Furstenberg +1 (845) 928 5745 ★ ★ ★ ★
Best known for her wrap dress, DVF sells her previous seasons' collections here with discounts from 25%, and up to 80% for older stock, alongside some shoes and accessories.

Dolce and Gabbana +1 (845) 928 5221 ★ ★ ★ ★
This trend setting Italian designer's previous seasons' men's and women's collections, along with a selection of accessories, are here; including watches and jewellery. Discounts of up to 50%.

Ellen Tracey +1 (845) 928 9097 ★ ★ ★ ★
The past seasons' womenswear along with accessories can be found here, discounted by 25% up to 80%.

Emilio Pucci +1 (845) 928 5138 ★ ★ ★ ★
The highly feminine and geometric collection of Pucci can be purchased, along with a full range of accessories, at discounts starting at 40% off the boutique price.

Escada Company Store +1 (845) 928 7199 ★ ★ ★ ★
The Escada collection along with Escada Sports (and accessories) are available with discounts starting at 60% and going as high as 80%; including shoes and bags from previous seasons' collections.

Etro +1 (845) 928 9256 ★ ★ ★ ★ ★
This Italian contemporary menswear collection with both casual and formal wear offers discounts of up to 50% off past collections.

Fendi +1 (845) 928 5455 ★ ★ ★ ★
This Italian luxury leather company has a good selection of handbags, watches, wallets and small leather goods at discounts starting from 30% to 70%.

Frette +1 (845) 928 4866 ★ ★ ★ ★
Spectacular bed linens and accessories from Italy can be found here, (including their Hotel collection) with discounts starting at 30% and going up to 75% on older stock.

Giorgio Armani +1 (845) 928 9400 ★ ★ ★ ★
The Armani collection, along with AX, Emporio and Armani jeans can be found here for both men and women at discounts of between 50% and 60%.

Gucci +1 (845) 928 8034 ★ ★ ★ ★

The Gucci outlet is one of only 3 in the US and has both men's and women's collections with good discounts of between 30% and 70%. However, the outlet does get very busy and sometimes you will have to wait to gain entrance.

Kate Spade +1 (845) 928 0864 ★ ★ ★ ★

The handbag, shoe and accessories collections, along with sunglasses and signature stationery from past collections, are available at discounts from 20% to 60%.

Lancôme – The Company Outlet +1 (845) 928 4323 ★ ★ ★ ★

The Company Outlet sells its products at 20% discount and has a good selection of skincare, beauty products, aftershaves and perfumes.

Longchamp +1 (845) 928 4727 ★ ★ ★ ★

The French brand offers handbags, travel bags, wallets, small leather goods and ready-to-wear, at discounts starting at 30% and going up to 60%.

Maxamara +1 (845) 928 4378 ★ ★ ★ ★

The outlet carries the full past season's collections for all 5 brands, (including Sportmax) with discounts on ready-to-wear at 40% and coats at 30%.

M Mossoni +1 (845) 928 6010 ★ ★ ★

This Italian brand has its knitted collection of men's and women's clothing here, along with their home collection. Reductions start at 40%.

Michael Kors +1 (845) 928 9236 ★ ★ ★

This outlet sells its lifestyle collection for women at discounts starting at 30%. The extensive range of accessories includes belts, bags, clutches and perfumes.

Neiman Marcus Last Call +1 (845) 928 4993 ★ ★ ★ ★ ★

A good range of clothing for men and women, including designer labels from Bergdoff Goodman in Manhattan, who send their sale stock here to clear. You will also find a large selection from the home collections, with discounts starting at 50%, but going up to an incredible 90%.

Oscar de la Renta +1 (845) 928 8106 ★ ★ ★ ★

This legend in the fashion world has its outlet shop here, selling previous collections of women's ready-to-wear. Discounts start at 50%.

OshKosh B'Gosh +1 (845) 928 4449 ★ ★ ★

This trendy children's range has discounts from 30% to 60% off the past seasons' collections, with clothing for boys and girls up to the age of 12.

Prada (Space) +1 (845) 928 3706 ★ ★ ★
This is the smallest of the Prada Space shops, containing collections of men's and womenswear, along with some leather goods and shoes. Discounts are generally around the 40% to 60% mark.

Pretesi +1 (845) 928 4810 ★ ★ ★
Bed linens and home accessories can be found here, along with tablemats and napkins, at discounts starting at 30% and going up to as much as 85%.

Roberto Cavalli +1 (845) 928 9116 ★ ★ ★ ★
The outlet here just carries the Roberto Cavalli collection for women and a small collection for men. These can be found at discounts of 50% off the boutique price but, periodically, you can find extra discounts with up to 75% off the outlet price.

St John Company Store +1 (845) 928 4452 ★ ★ ★
The outlet's stock is about six months behind the retail boutiques, and carries the collection along with shoes, belts and jewellery, at 50% of the RRP.

Swarovski +1 (845) 928 1003 ★ ★ ★ ★
The outlet mainly sells 'retired' jewellery from its collections at discounts that start at 30% of the original selling price.

Theory Men +1 (845) 928 4825 ★ ★ ★
The outlet sells business and casual wear for men, at discounts starting at 40% off the retail price.

Tory Burch +1 (845) 928 2886 ★ ★ ★ ★
The lifestyle collections, including sportswear and accessories, can be bought at discounts of up to 40% off the normal boutique prices.

True Religion +1 (845) 928 5441 ★ ★ ★ ★ ★
This American made designer jeans outlet has some great buys on denim for men, women and children. They stock most sizes, have helpful staff, and discounts start at 50%.

Ugg +1 (845) 928 9981 ★ ★ ★
The Australian phenomenon has its outlet shops selling boots for men, women and children. Discounts start at 10% and go up to 50%.

Valentino +1 (845) 928 0820 ★ ★ ★ ★
Men's and women's collections are displayed alongside watches, eyewear, ties and men's shoes.
Discounts start at 40% and go as high as 75% during its sale.

Victorinox Swiss Army +1 (845) 928 0600 ★ ★ ★ ★
This outlet has a great selection of the famous Swiss luggage, along with outdoor clothing and
accessories. Victorinox always has offers and promotions, discounting some items down to an
astounding 80%.

William Sonoma Outlet +1 (845) 928 4956 ★ ★ ★ ★ ★
This boutique chain of kitchen accessories shops has a very large outlet at Woodbury selling all its
previous seasons' and discontinued lines; including cookware and some home electrical stock at
discounts of up to 75% off the RRP.

Yves St Laurent Rive Gauche +1 (845) 928 2169 ★ ★ ★ ★
The men's and women's collections from previous seasons are here along with shoes and bags at
discounts starting at 30% and going up to 60%.

Also Here

Adidas
Aeropostale
Aerosoles
AG Adriano Goldschmied
Aldo
American Apparel
Ann Taylor Factory Store
Anne Fontaine
Anne Klein
Armani Exchange
Ashworth-Callaway Golf
Bally
Banana Republic
Bass
BCBG Max Azria
Bebe
Benetton
Bose
Bottega Veneta
Brighton Collectibles
Brooks Brothers Factory Store
Burberry

Burberry Clearance Outlet
Calvin Klein Men's
Calvin Klein Women's
Carter's
Catherine Malandrino
Chico's
Chloé
Claire's Accessories
Clarks Bostonian
Coach
Cole Haan
Corningware Corelle Revere
Crabtree & Evelyn
Crate and Barrel
Designer Fragrances
Diesel
Dior
Disney Store Outlet
DKNY
DKNY Jeans
Dooney & Bourke
Easy Spirit
ECCO
Ecko Unltd
Eddie Bauer Outlet
Elie Tahari
Esprit
Factory Brand Shoes
Fossil
French Connection
Furla
G-Star Raw
Gap
Geoffrey Beene
Geox
Giuseppe Zanotti Design
Godiva Chocolatier
Greg Norman
Guess
Guess Accessories
Gymboree Outlet
Harry & David
Headline News

Helmut Lang
Hickey Freeman/Bobby Jones
Hugo Boss
Izod
J Crew
J Crew/Crewcuts
Jimmy Choo
JM Originals
Jockey
Joe's Jeans
Johnston & Murphy
Jones New York
Jones New York Sport & Country
Jones New York Woman
Journeys
Judith Leiber
Judith Ripka
Juicy Couture
Kasper
KB Toy Outlet
Kenneth Cole
Kensie
Kipling
La Perla
Lacoste
Le Creuset
L'eggs Hanes Bali Playtex
Le Gourmet Chef
Lenox
LeSportsac
Levi's/Dockers Outlet by Most
Lids for Less
Liz Claiborne
Lladró
L'Occitane
Loro Piana
Lucky Brand Jeans
Maidenform
MaxStudio.com
Michael Kors
Miss Sixty/Energie
Movado Company Store
Naturalizer

Nautica
NauticaKids
Nike Factory Store
Nine West
Oakley Vault
PacSun
Perfumania
Perry Ellis
Polo Ralph Lauren Factory Store
Polo Ralph Lauren Children
Puma
Quiksilver
Ralph Lauren Factory Store
Ralph Lauren Home Factory Store
Reebok
Rochester Big & Tall
Rockford Footwear Depot
Rockport
Royal Doulton
Saks Fifth Avenue Off 5th
Salvatore Ferragamo
Samsonite
Sarar
Seiko The Company Store
Sketchers
Solstice Sunglass Outlet
Sony
Spyder
Stride Rite Keds Sperry
Sunglass Hut
Sunglass Station
TAG Heuer
Tahari
The Children's Place Outlet
The Cosmetics Company Store
The London Jewelry Collection
The Luggage Factory
The North Face
Theory
Thomas Pink
Timberland
Time Factory Watch Outlet
Tod's

Tommy Bahama
Tommy Hilfiger
Tommy Kids
Totes/ Isotoners/ Sunglass World
TSE Cashmere
Tumi
Ultra Diamonds
Under Armour
Van Heusen
Versace
Vineyard Vines
Vitamin World
Waterford Wedgwood
Wolford
World of Fun
Yankee Candle
Gauche
Zales Outlet
Zegna

Independent Outlets

Listed here are four Manhattan chain stores that specialise in discounted goods. Although they are not truly independents, this is the nearest thing to warehouse shopping in the Big Apple.

Century 21 ★ ★ ★ ★
22 Courtland Street, New York, NY 10007
At Broadway
Telephone +1 212 227 9092
www.c21stores.com

Opening Hours:
Mon-Wed 7:45-9
Thurs-Fri 7:45-9:30
Sat 10-9
Sun 11-8

Established for over 40 years, this store has become a New York icon for designer deals, with discounts from 40%-70% on end-of-lines and samples. Featuring men's, women's and children's clothing, shoes and accessories as well as items for the home. The shop gets very crowded and has no changing rooms, but items can be returned. A great resource if you only want to shop in Manhattan.

Daffys ★ ★ ★
www.daffys.com
8 Locations across the City
(check website for addresses and opening times)

The slogan is 'High fashion – Low prices'. You will need to put aside some time to go through the many clothing rails to be found here. The entire family are catered for and you can find some amazing buys. Discounts start at 50% off the original prices but can be as much as 90%.

Filene's Basement ★★★
4 Union Square South, New York, NY 10003
Telephone +1 212 358 0169
www.filenesbasement.com

Opening hours:
Mon-Sat: 9-10
Sun: 11-7

The first branch of this famous chain store opened in 1908 in Boston. There are now more than 31 branches across the US. Their famous Automatic Markdown Plan means that the longer they stock an item, the bigger the discount on it. Men's, women's and children's clothing, along with accessories and home items, can be found at huge discounts.

Loehmann's ★★★
101 Seventh Avenue, New York, NY10011
Telephone +1 212 352 0856
www.loehmanns.com

This branch of Loehmann's has a good selection of clothing for the entire family at discounts starting at 30% and rising to as much as 90%. There is also a branch at 2101 Broadway, on the Upper West Side..

Hong Kong

Although times have changed with the handing over of Hong Kong to China in 1997, Hong Kong still offers shoppers a good selection of retail outlets. For example, the electrical goods shops and tailors of Nathan Road in Kowloon still offer the most amazing deals. The skilled tailors are able to quickly copy and make up your favourite designer outfit. Unless you are adventurous, we suggest staying in the centre of the city (Central); the outlying neighbourhoods can be a little intimidating to the western traveller. The cheapest forms of travel in the city are by trains and taxis. If you're flying in, the new Airport Express is by far the easiest and cheapest way of getting into the city. All road signs are in Chinese and English. The border area with China has become a mecca for discounted goods and bargain shopping and is four hours from Hong Kong.

How to get there

Cathay Pacific
London to Hong Kong return ticket including surcharges and tax, approximately £750
(Prices vary according to travel dates and length of advanced booking)

Typical price for a 4 night stay:
Hotel and flight package approximately £900 (www.ebookers.com)

Where to stay

Central Park Hotel
263 Hollywood Road, Central
Telephone: +852 2850 8899
Email: enquiry@centralparkhotel.com.hk
3 stars, clean with small rooms, recently modernised. Located in the antiques and collectables area of Hong Kong. Booked via the internet at £65 per night.

The Mandarin Oriental HK
5 Connaught Road, Central
Telephone:. +852 2825 4888
Email: mohkg-reservations@mohg.com
If you are looking to treat yourself, this is the place to stay. A study room with queen bed starts at £180 per night. Great location. Close to shopping, ferries and trains.

Transportation

Trains from Hong Kong International Airport to the centre of Hong Kong are HK$100 each way. Taxis are very cheap. The Star Ferry, which travels between Hong Kong and Kowloon costs HK$2.60 each way and takes 5 minutes.

Information

The Hong Kong tourism office has a comprehensive and accessible website at www.HKTO.com, which will offer you lots of help in planning your trip. The guidebook used on this trip was the Lonely Planet guide to Hong Kong and Macau, which we would recommend reading before you travel.

Independent Outlets

Horizon Plaza
2 Lee Wing Street, Ap Lei Chau, Hong Kong
Horizon Plaza houses many of the trade showrooms for the furniture business. They are happy to sell direct to the public however, as are the 5 outlets listed below.

How to get there:

Horizon Plaza is situated near the Aberdeen district of Hong Kong and is a 20 minute cab ride from Central at HK$75.00.
Cabs wait outside the Horizon Plaza. They will take you back into the city or on to the nearby Prada outlet.

Bluebell Fashion Warehouse ★★
(Room number 1017)
Telephone: +852 2580 1722
Stocks: Jimmy Choo, Moschino, Anna Molinari Blumarine, Paul Smith
This small showroom has a limited selection from each of the above designer's past seasons. You can find great discounts here.

Fairton Labels Fashion Warehouse ★★★
(Room number 1910-11)
Telephone: +852 2873 2230
Stocks: Lloyd, Kookai, Pollini, and Jean Paul Gautier.
Fairton carries a good selection of past seasons' womenswear in the above 5 labels and just one for men (JPG), at discounts of up to 80%.

JJ Brothers Tailors ★★★
The Ritz Carlton Hotel, 3 Connaught Road
Telephone: +852 2526 8813
This small operation in the lobby of the Ritz offers a fine service for both men and women with a good selection of fabrics, with a fast turnaround.

Joyce Warehouse ★★★★★
(Room number 2102)
Telephone: +852 2814 8313
Joyce has four shops in the Hong Kong area, and last seasons' collections are sent to this warehouse to clear. Items are discounted in direct proportion to the length of time they remain in the warehouse. Prices can be reduced as much as 80% for older stock. You will find merchandise here by Anna Sui, Dries Van Norton, Etro, Jil Sander, Marni, See by Chloe and Viktor and Rolf. Well worth a visit.

Lane Crawford ★ ★ ★ ★
(25th floor)
Telephone: +852 2118 2150
This famous Hong Kong department store opened its first outlet 4 years ago, and carries a good selection of women's and men's clothing and shoes, as well as furniture and accessories at greatly reduced prices. Additional discount is given on stock that is more than a season old.

Nathan Road, Kowloon ★ ★ ★ ★
This very busy street houses a vast array of electrical outlets selling everything at discount prices, although it is common practice to haggle down prices even further. It is important to check your purchases before you leave the shop; some complaints of items being switched at the counter have been reported.

Sam's Tailor ★ ★ ★ ★
94 Nathan Road, Tsim Sha Tsui, Kowloon
Telephone: +852 2367 9423/2721
Sam's are world renowned for their copies of famous designer names, and the very busy shop in Burlington Arcade is catering to businessmen and tourist alike. Plan to visit early in your trip, as most garments will require two fittings, but conveniently, can be copied and turned around in a few days.

Space (Prada) ★ ★ ★
2F Marina Square, East Commercial Block, South Horizons, Aberdeen
Telephone: +852 2814 9576
The Prada outlet in Hong Kong is in the Aberdeen residential area, with access to the store via two internal escalators. A large selection of men and women's fashion and some accessories are sold here, but Space doesn't necessarily have the best prices for Prada and Mui Mui.

Outlet Villages

Citygate Outlet
20 Tat Tung Road, Tung Chung, Lantau
Telephone: +852 2109 2933
Citygate is located 40 minutes from Central on the Tung Chung line and the mall is situated above the station.

We would rate this outlet highly and have featured 5 of the best shops below. There is also a movie theatre, a number of restaurants and coffee shops and an extensive supermarket on the lower ground floor.

How to get there:

MTR Exit C at Tung Chung Station of Tung Chung Line.

Top 5

Bauhaus Outlet – Unit 250 ★★★
Sport outfitters Bauhaus has a good selection of sportswear. It also sells outdoor clothing for men, women and children.

Folli Follie Outlet – Unit 205 ★★★
Here you can find a good selection of jewellery, watches and accessories from the Folli Follie collection (up to 60% off).

IT Outlet – Unit G01 ★★★
This large outlet shop has a big selection of designer labels (some reduced by up to 80%). Dolce and Gabbana often has huge reductions.

Kate Spade ★★★★
New York Kate Spade – Unit 220
Sells her range of handbags, shoes and accessories of up to 50% off past seasons' collections.

Vivienne Tam Outlet – Unit 245 ★★★★
Designer Vivienne Tam's samples, overruns and previous seasons' collections are sold off at a discount of up to 60%

Also Here:

Adidas Outlet
Bally
Benetton Outlet
Calvin Klein Underwear
City Chain outlet
Clarks Outlet
Columbia Factory Outlet
D'urban (coming soon)

Esprit Outlet
Evita Perini Outlet
Giordano Outlet
Jill Stuart Outlet (coming soon)
K Swiss Outlet
Kent & Curwen (coming soon)
Kingkow Outlet
KNJI Design Accessories Outlet
La Compagnie Des Petits Outlet
Lafuma Outlet
Lanvin
Last Call (Callaway and Pearly Gates)
Laura Ashley
LensCrafters
Levi's Outlet
Lids Outlet
MaBelle Outlet
Mirabell Outlet
Moiselle Outlet
Nautica Outlet
New Balance Outlet
Nike Factory Outlet
Optical 88 Outlet
Polo Ralph Lauren Factory Store
Quiksilver Outlet
Rabeanco Outlet
Samsonite
Seven7 Outlet
The Body Shop Outlet
Timberland Outlet
Time+style Outlet
Triumph Outlet (coming soon)

HER MAJESTY'S FORCES SERVICE
Sam's
TAILOR
T.S.T.P.O.BOX 95392
BURLINGTON ARCADE "K-1
92-94 NATHAN ROAD
KOWLOON, HONG KONG
Specially
MR.

Florence

Florence is famous for its exquisite art and magnificent architecture. Although it is not considered to be the fashion capital of Italy, it is a wonderful shopping city in its own right. The centre of Florence, along with its amazing sights and excellent places to eat, is home to the city's many markets, which offer a great selection of merchandise but have become particularly famous for leather goods and stationery. Forty minutes outside the city (and well worth a visit) lies the flagship Prada outlet, which is housed in a corner of their distribution warehouse. You can also find one of Dolce and Gabbana's premier outlets on the outskirts of the city. We always suggest double-checking the opening times of these and other outlets as many don't open on Mondays until 3:30pm.

If you are a really serious shopper, our day trip may appeal; fly out, shop and return the same day! However, be warned; this trip is not for the faint-hearted. But with such fantastic shopping opportunities, you will be able to save a small fortune and your day around some of the finest Italian shopping outlets will be a day to remember.

How to get there

Flights from London Gatwick to Pisa with BA, including surcharges and taxes, are approximately £150 return.

Flights from London Gatwick to Florence on Meridiana Airlines (www.meridiana.it) are available at approximately £200 return.

Flights from London Stansted to Pisa with Ryanair are approximately £60 return.

Transportation

Car Hire

Argusrentals.com
Pick up 10am drop off 9pm (Pisa)
Between £30-£40 Daily

Florence in a Day!

Yes, it can be done – fly out of Gatwick in the early morning to Pisa, then return in the evening on the last flight back. To get the best out of the day, we would advise you hiring a car from the airport. On the test run, we managed to see every outlet that is listed in the Florence section – 130 to be exact, and found some great buys. A little exhausting, but great fun.

Have lunch at the Space Café at Prada, or grab a bite to eat at The Mall. The Barberino designer outlet has a number of food outlets and also a great pizzeria, Restaurante le Capennine (very popular with the locals, so it has to be good).

A great local spot is Cibreo Restaurant (Via Andrea del Verrocchio 8r, 50122. Tel: 055 234 11 00) in Florence's city centre. There is also an agreeable trattoria and a café across the road from Cibreo.

However, we recommend getting back to Pisa for supper. The self-service restaurant at Pisa Airport is fine, but there is a very pleasant table service restaurant, serving good food, next door.

Ideally, there should be two of you sharing our 'day trip' experience. One person to drive and one to keep an eye out on the traffic signs! Our round trip for the day cost 60 euros in petrol, but when you compare that to the handmade pair of Gucci shoes we bought for only £50, it was well worth the expense.

If you don't want to drive, it would be possible to get around using a combination of trains and taxis, but it would be much more wearying and probably more expensive.

Independent Outlets

Dolce & Gabbana ★ ★ ★ ★
Localita Santa Maria Maddalena, Via Piana dell'Isola 49, Rignano sull'Arno
Telephone +39 055 833 13 00
www.dolcegabbana.com

Opening Hours:
Mon-Sat 9-7
Sun 3-7

How to get there:

By Car - Take the Leccio turning off the A1, then 1/2km to 1km south of Leccio, turn right (follow the Fendi outlet signs) until you arrive at a T-Junction. On your left is a long building with no signs – this is the Dolce & Gabbana outlet.

By Train - Florence to Rome line. Get off at Rignano sull'Arno then taxi for 4km south.

This smart outlet is located at the front of the factory and offers a large selection of men's and women's ready-to-wear clothing, along with full lines of past seasons' accessories, plus shoes and boots for both sexes. The discounts start at 40% and depending on the time of year you can find really great bargains.

Roberto Cavalli ★ ★ ★ ★
Via Volturno 3/3 50019, Sesto Fiorentino, Osmannoro
Telephone: +39 055 317754
www.robertocavallioutlet.it

Opening Hours:
Mon-Sat 10-7

How to get there:

By Car - Take the A1 north from Florence to the Sesto Fiorentino exit, (the exit is before you get on the motorway) then follow the indications for Osmannoro. After the underpass the outlet is on the right.

The outlet opened in 2002 and carries just the Roberto Cavalli women's range. It offers a good selection of ready-to-wear from last seasons' collection. It also sells bags, small accessories and some jewellery. Discounts start at 50% off the boutique price, and up to an additional 60% off for older items.

Space (Prada) ★ ★ ★ ★ ★
Localita Levanella, Montevarchi
Telephone: +39 055 919 01
www.prada.com
Opening hours:
Mon-Sat: 9:30-7
Sunday: 3-7

How to get there:

By Car- Follow the SS69 south from Leccio to Montevarchi (28km). Go south through the town to Levanella. Turn left at Via Levanella Becorpi (passing the warehouses) to the car park at the end of the street. If you pass under the railway bridge on the SS69 you have overshot the turn off by a few hundred metres.

By Train- Take an Arezzo bound train from Florence, get off at Montevarchi and take a taxi.

This outlet was extensively renovated last November, bringing it in line with the new design of all Prada shops worldwide. The store has all the Prada collections, (including Sport) with extensive collections from past seasons. It also has a large shoe department, along with accessories, bags, some luggage and fragrances. Discounts start at 40%. You can find one-off samples in the outlet, which can be identified by a code number starting with a Z. If you are a Prada fan, this is the pre-eminent outlet out of the 7 worldwide, and is well worth making the trek.

Outlet Villages

Barberino Designer Outlet
Via Meucci snc 50031, Barberino del Mugello
Telephone: +39 055 842 161
www.mcarthurglen.it

Opening Hours:
Tues-Fri 10-8
Sat-Sun 10-9
Mon 2-8
during January, June, July, August, September and December.

How to get there:

By Car - take the SS65 Starda Statale Bolognese as far as Fiesole, then follow the signs for San Piero a Sieve/Barberino di Mugello.

Top 10

Bric's Store ★★★
The Italian luggage company has a good selection of suitcases, along with holdalls and small leather goods, with discounts starting at 40% and going up to 75% off the RRP.

Calvin Klein Collections ★★★★
The men's and women's collection are found here at discounts of up to 75%, along with some accessories, formal wear and suits.

Class Roberto Cavalli ★★★★
This is a new outlet and carries the more reasonably priced range of Cavalli for women, with shoes and accessories. Discounts start at 50%.

Dolce and Gabbana ★ ★ ★ ★
If you can't get to the main outlet store, this large outlet carries a good range of the collections for both men and women, at discounts starting at 40% and rising.

Grigioperla ★ ★ ★ ★
This menswear collection offers its loungewear, underwear and swimming trunk collection at great savings, along with some casual clothing, at discounts starting at 40%.

Guess Kids ★ ★ ★ ★
The American brand has wonderful outlets for children with a good selection of discounted goods for both boys and girls.

KIDS ★ ★ ★
The outlet sells 5 lines of past seasons' collections with discounts starting at 50% off Escada, DNKY, Timberland, Elle and Marithe + Francois Guribaud.

Malo ★ ★ ★
Luxury cashmere, some small leather goods, and a small menswear collection from past seasons can be found at good discounts starting at 50%.

M Missoni ★ ★ ★ ★
The signature knits of this classic Italian designer can be found here along with the home collection at discounts starting at 40% and rising.

Prada ★ ★ ★
The store has a small selection of men's and women's ready-to-wear, along with great deals on a small selection of footwear. Discounts are the same as the Montivarchi outlet but here the selection is much smaller.

Also Here

Abital
Adidas
Arfango
Baldinini
Black Box
Bose
Bottega Verde
Brooksfield
Bruno Magli
Calzedonia
Calvin Klein Jeans

Calvin Klein Underwear
Caractere
Carlo Pignatelli
C'E Bassetti
Clan International (Belstaff/ Capalbio)
Coccinelle
Colombo Collezioni in Cachemire
Compagnia Celle Pelli
Corso Roma
Cotton Belt
David Mayer
Diesel Kids Temporary Store
Diffusione Tessile
Docksteps
Douglas
Elena Miro'
Eredi Pisano'
Fila
Fornarina
Frette
Furla
Gas
Guinti Al Punto
Golden Lady
Guess
Guess Accessories
Guru
Il Lanificio
Jean's Paul Gaultier
John Ashfield
Kathy Van Zeeland
La Casa Italiana
Lagostina
Laltramoda
Les Copains
Levi's – Dockers
Lovable Playtex Planet
Malloy
Mariella Burani
Marlboro Classic
Massimo Rebecchi
Maui Bear
Moreschi

Motivi
Motostore
Nautica
Officina Di Ricerca (Moschino Jeans, DKNY, Krizia Jeans)
Pal Zileri
Pinko
Piquadro
Pollini
Polo Ralph Lauren
Puma
Pupa Outlet
Q Come Quore
RCR – Royal Cristal Rock
Richmond
Rifle
Robe Di Kappa
Rocco Bormioli
Segue
Sia
Slam
Sony Playstation
Stefanel
Store House (Barbour, Woolrich)
St. Diego–A-Style
Sunglass Time
Tailor Club
The Bridge
The End
Timberland
Ugo Colella
United Colours of Benetton
Vestebene
Wrangler – Lee

The Mall
Via Europa 8
Leccio
Reggello 50060
Florence

How to get there:

By Car - take the A1 motorway (towards Florence/ Rome from Milan or towards Florence from Rome) and take the exit marked Incisa. Stay on the right towards Pontassieve until reaching Leccio. Soon after passing the centre of Leccio, The Mall will be on the left.

By Train - from Florence's Santa Maria Novella station to Rignano sull'Arno and then taxi (about 5 minutes).

By Bus - there is a daily shuttle bus service that takes about an hour. It leaves from Florence station and drops you at The Mall. Contact +39 055 8657775 Monday to Friday 9am to 6pm for information. There is also a public bus service from Florence to The Mall run by Sita Bus Company – price 2.90 per person, one-way fare (pick up - Autostazione Sita, Via S Caterina da Siena 17).

Opening Hours:
Mon-Sat 9- 7
Sun 3-7

Top Ten

Alexander McQueen/Stella McCartney/Balenciaga ★ ★ ★ ★ ★
This shop is crammed full of these 3 designers' past seasons' collections. Womenswear is predominantly featured, but there are some menswear items, too. Discounts of up to 75% off the RRP.

Bottega Veneta ★ ★ ★ ★
The past seasons' men's and women's ready-to-wear collections are featured, as well as bags, leather goods and shoes with discounts starting at 40%.

Ermenegildo Zegna ★ ★ ★ ★
This high-end men's collection sells at discounts of up to 60% and includes casual and formal wear, along with some accessories.

Fendi ★ ★ ★ ★
The Fendi shop moved into The Mall a couple of years ago and has a full range of past and ready-to-wear collections, at discounts starting at 40% and rising.

Gucci ★★★★★
This is one of only 3 outlets in Italy and has a great selection of bags, shoes and accessories, along with men's and women's ready-to-wear collections from past seasons, and some samples. Discounts of up to 70% off.

I Pinco Pallino ★★★★
This high-end children's outfitter has a good selection for boys, girls and newborns, with discounts starting at 40% off past collections.

Marni ★★★★
The collections are discounted up to 50% off the retail price for both the men's and women's collections, along with some accessories.

Sergio Rosso ★★★★
This high-end shoe chain has its outlet selling previous seasons' collections, with discounts starting at 40% off the boutique prices.

Tod's and Hogan ★★★★
A great selection of Tod's and Hogan footwear, bags, and accessories, along with small leather goods, can be discounted up to 75% off the RRP. Great deals when stock gets low.

Yohiji Yamamotto ★★★★
The Japanese designer has a good selection of past seasons' collections at discounts starting at 50%.

Also Here:

Burberry
Emanuel Ungaro
Giorgio Armani
Hogan
La Perla
Loro Piana
Pucci
Salvatore Ferragamo
Valentino
Yves Saint Laurent

British & International Outlet Villages

Brand/Retailer	Brand Category	Top 10 Outlet & UK Independents	International & Independents	Page no.
Arbital	Fashion		B	147
Accessorize	Shoes & Accessories	B		49
Adidas	Sportswear	CO Y A GQ CV	B CO W	52
Aeropostale	Fashion		W	126
Aerosoles	Shoes & Accessories		W	126
AG Adriano Goldschmied	Fashion		W	126
Agatha	Accessories		CO	138
Agent Provocateur	Fashion	B		44
Alan Paine	Fashion	I		12
Aldo	Shoes & Accessories		W	126
Alexander McQueen	Fashion		M	150
Alexon	Fashion	S CV		69
All Saints	Fashion	CO B		49
All Wellan Good	Beauty	FB		80
American Apparel	Fashion		W	126
Andrew Elliot Ltd	Accessories/Home	I		12
Animal	Fashion	CO A GQ		66
Ann Taylor Factory Store	Fashion		W	126
Anne Fontaine	Fashion	B	W	126
Anne Klein	Fashion		W	126
Antler	Shoes & Accessories	CO Y A S GQ L FB I		12
Anya Hindmarch	Shoes & Accessories	B		45
Aquascutum	Fashion	B S L I		12
Arfango	Fashion/Shoes/Accessories		B	147
Armani Collections/DKNY	Fashion	L Y		52

Brand/Retailer	Brand Category	Top 10 Outlet & UK Independents	International & Independents	Page no.
Armani Exchange	Fashion		W CO	126
Armani Jeans	Fashion		M	151
Arthur Price	Home	I		13
Artigiano	Fashion	CV W		73
Ashworth-Galloway Golf	Fashion		W	126
aspex contemporary art gallery	Art/Gifts	GQ		66
Austin Reed	Fashion	CO Y S GQ FB I		13
Autonomy	Fashion	CO Y A S L CV FB		76
Aynsley China	Home/Gifts	I		13
Bags Etc	Shoes & Accessories	GQ L CV FB		65
Baggage Factory	Accessories	W		85
Baldinini	Shoes & Accessories		B	147
Balenciaga	Fashion		M	150
Bally	Shoes & Accessories	B	W CO	49
Banana Books	Books	W		85
Banana Republic	Fashion	GQ	W	64
Barbour	Fashion	GQ FB		80
Barker Shoes	Shoes & Accessories	I		13
Barneys New York Outlet	Fashion		W	122
Baronjon	Fashion	CO A FB		61
Bass	Fashion		W	126
Battersea Candle Shop	Home	I		14
Bauhaus	Fashion		CO	137
BCBG Max Azria	Fashion		W	126
Bebe	Fashion		W	126

Brand/Retailer	Brand Category	Top 10 Outlet & UK Independents	International & Independents	Page no.
Bedeck	Home	GQ L CV Y CO		65
Belinda Robertson Ltd	Fashion/Accessories	I		14
Ben Sherman	Fashion	CO Y A S L		59
Bench & Hooch	Fashion	CO Y A GQ L		60
Benetton	Fashion	A CV	W CO	60
Berry Bros. & Rudd	Food	I		14
Betsey Johnson	Fashion		W	122
Brand Alley	Fashion	WWW		115
Bijoux	Shoes & Accessories	FB		81
Billabong	Fashion	CO S CV FB		56
Billie and Gruff Cashmere & More	Fashion	Y		54
Billion Dollar Babes	Fashion	SS		110
Birthdays	Gifts	Y		54
Black & Decker	Home	L		76
Black Box	Fashion		B	147
Bluebell Fashion Warehouse	Fashion/Shoes		I	135
Boden	Fashion/Shoes/Accessories	S		105
Bodum	Home/Gifts	B		49
Bonpoint	Children	B		45
Bookends	Books	A		61
Books Etc	Books	B		45
Bose	Home/Fashion	B CO Y A FB GQ	B W	56
Bottega Veneta	Fashion/Luggage		W M	122
Bottega Verde	Home/Gifts		B	147
Brand Fusion	Sportswear	L FB CO		77
Bric's Store	Shoes & Accessories		B	146

Brand/Retailer	Brand Category	Top 10 Outlet & UK Independents	International & Independents	Page no.
Brighton Collectibles	Accessories		W	126
Brooks Brothers Factory Store	Fashion		W	126
Brooksfield	Fashion		B	147
Browns Labels for Less	Fashion	I		14
Brunello Cucinelli	Fashion		W	122
Bruno Magli	Shoes & Accessories		B	147
Burberry	Fashion	B CO Y S GQ FB I	W M	14
Burleigh	Home/Gifts	I		15
Cadbury Factory Shop	Food	CO Y S L CV FB GQ		59
Café Cotton	Fashion	B		50
Calvin Klein	Fashion	B FB CV		72
Calvin Klein Jeans	Fashion	CO Y L	W CO B	146
Calvin Klein Men's	Fashion		W	127
Calvin Klein Underwear	Underwear	B CO Y S GQ A	B CO	50
Calvin Klein Women's	Fashion		W	127
Calzedonia	Underwear		B	147
Camille	Underwear	W FB		85
Camper	Shoes & Accessories	B		45
Caractère	Fas		B	148
Carlo Pignatelli	Fashion		B	148
Caroline Charles	Fashion	I		15

KEY TO OUTLETS

Brand/Retailer	Brand Category	Top 10 Outlet & UK Independents	International & Independents	Page no.
Carphone Warehouse	Technology/Gifts	CO A S GQ		69
Carter's	Children		W	127
Caspian Sea Caviar	Food	I		15
Cath Kidston	Home	B		45
Catherine Malandrino	Fashion		W	127
Catwalk To Closet	Fashion/Shoes/Accessories	www		115
C'è Bassetti	Home/Gifts		B	147
Cecil Gee	Fashion	CO		59
Celine	Fashion	B	W	45
Century 21	Fashion/Shoes/Accessories		I	130
Cerruti 1881 Menswear	Fashion	B		50
CH Carolina Herrera	Fashion		W	122
Chanel	Fashion		W	122
Chapelle Jewellery	Jewellry	CO Y A S GQ L CV W FB		59
Charcoal & Chalk	Fashion	Y		54
Charles Clinkard	Shoes & Accessories	L		78
Charles Tyrwhitt	Fashion	B CO S		56
Chelsea Textiles	Home	S		105
Chickeeduck	Children		CO	138
Chico's	Fashion		W	127
Chilli Pepper	Fashion	Y W		59
China China	Home	Y		54
China Place	Home/Gifts	A		61
Chloé	Fashion		W	122

Brand/Retailer	Brand Category	Top 10 Outlet & UK Independents	International & Independents	Page no.
Chomette Dornberger	Home	I		15
Christopher Wray Lighting	Home	I		16
Christy Towels	Home	CO Y A S GQ L CV FB		80
Church's English Shoes	Shoes & Accessories	B I		16
Churchill China Outlet Centre Superstore	Home/Gifts	I		16
City Chain	Accessories		CO	137
Claire's Accessories	Accessories	CO Y A S GQ L CV W FB	W	59
Clan International (Belstaff/Capalbio)	Fashion		B	148
Clarks	Shoes & Accessories	B CO Y A S GQ L CV FB	CO	137
Clarks Bostonian	Shoes & Accessories		W	127
Clinton Cards	Gifts	GQ W		66
Club 21	Fashion/Children		CO	138
Coach	Luggage/Accessories		W	127
Coast	Fashion	B CO Y CV		52
Coccinelle	Shoes & Accessories	Y	B	148
Cole Haan	Accessories/Home		W	127
Colefax and Fowler	Fashion	SS		110
Collector's Store	Fashion	A		62
Colombo Collezioni in Cachemire	Fashion		B	148
Columbia	Fashion		CO	137
Compagnia delle Pelli	Shoes & Accessories		B	148
Contract Candles	Shoes & Accessories	I		16
Converse	Fashion		W	123

Brand/Retailer	Brand Category	Top 10 Outlet & UK Independents	International & Independents	Page no.
Corningware Corelle Revere	Fashion		W	127
Corso Roma	Shoes & Accessories		B	148
Cosmetics Company	Beauty	Y		54
Cotswold Outdoor - Rock Bottom	Outdoor/Sportswear	I		17
Cotton Belt	Fashion		B	148
Cotton Traders	Fashion	CO Y A S GQ L CV W FB		59
Covent Garden Flower Market	Gifts	I		17
Crabtree & Evelyn	Beauty	GQ CV	W	72
Craghoppers	Outdoor/Sportswear	Y		54
Crate and Barrel	Home		W	127
Crew Clothing Co.	Fashion	Y S GQ CV FB		54
Crockett & Jones	Shoes & Accessories	I		17
Cross	Home	CO		59
Cruise	Fashion	L	W	127
D Selling Diesel	Fashion	FB		80
D2	Fashion	CO W		85
Daffys	Fashion		I	130
Daily Candy		www		116
Daks	Fashion	Y		52
Daniel Footwear	Shoes & Accessories	CO Y L		59
Daniel James Jewellery	Shoes & Accessories	GQ		66
Dar Lighting	Home	I		17
Darlington Crystal	Home/Gifts	CV I		18
David Clulow	Shoes & Accessories	B		50
David Mayer	Fashion		B	148

Brand/Retailer	Brand Category	Top 10 Outlet & UK Independents	International & Independents	Page no.
David Oliver Designer Outlet	Fashion	I		18
Denby	Home	CO Y A S GQ FB I		18
Denner Cashmere Warehouse	Fashion	I		18
Dents	Accessories	I		20
Descamps	Home	B Y		53
Design House	Home	A		62
Designer Fragrances	Beauty		W	127
Designer Kidz	Children	CO Y A L		76
Designer Me Out	Fashion	WWW		116
Designer Room	Fashion	CO Y A S L W FB		59
Designer Sales UK	Fashion/Shoes/Accessories	SS		109
Designer Warehouse Sales	Fashion	SS		108
Dexam International Ltd	Home	I		20
Diane Von Furstenberg	Fashion		W	123
Dible & Roy	Home	I		20
Dickinson	Fashion		CO	138
Diesel	Fashion	B CO FB	W	127
Diesel Kids	Children		B	148
Diffusione Tessile	Fashion/Shoes/Accessories		B	148
Dilemna Artwork	Home	Y		54
Dior	Fashion	B	W	45
Direct Cosmetics	Beauty	I		20
Direct Electrical Sales Ltd	Technology	I		20

Brand/Retailer	Brand Category	Top 10 Outlet & UK Independents	International & Independents	Page no.
Disney Store Outlet	Children		W	127
DKNY	Fashion	B	W	76
DKNY Jeans	Fashion		W	127
Docksteps	Shoes/Accessories		B	148
Dolce & Gabbana	Fashion	B	W B I	47
Donnay	Sports	CO Y A S GQ L FB		77
Dooney & Bourke	Luggage		W	127
Double Two	Fashion	Y CV W FB		54
Douglas	Beauty		B	148
Doulton and Company	Home	S I		21
Dune	Shoes & Accessories	CO GQ		64
Dunhill	Fashion	B		47
D'urban	Fashion		CO	138
Duty Free	Accessories	I		21
Early Learning Centre	Children	CO		56
East	Fashion	CO		59
EasyLiving Furniture	Furniture	W		84
Easy Spirit	Shoes & Accessories		W	127
Ebay	General	www		113
ECCO	Shoes & Accessories	CO A GQ CV		60
Ecko Unltd	Fashion		W	127
Eddie Bauer Outlet	Fashion		W	127
Elena Miro'	Fashion		B	148
Elie Tahari	Fashion		W	127
Ellen Tracy	Fashion		W	123
Emanuel Ungaro	Fashion		M	151

Brand/Retailer	Brand Category	Top 10 Outlet & UK Independents	International & Independents	Page no.
Emilio Pucci	Fashion		W M	123
Emma Bridgewater	Home	I		21
Emma Somerset	Fashion/Accessories	W		84
Emporio Home	Home	S W		78
Eredi Pisano'	Fashion		B	148
Escada Company Store	Fashion		W	123
Esprit	Fashion		W CO	127
Etro	Fashion		W	123
Event Jewellery	Jewellry	CV		74
Evisu/Stone Island	Fashion	S		68
Evita Peroni	Accessories		CO	138
Factory Brand Shoes	Shoes & Accessories		W	127
Fairton Labels Fashion Warehouse	Fashion		I	135
Famous Footwear	Shoes & Accessories	Y		54
Fashion Confidential	Fashion	WWW		114
Fashion Mag Daily	Fashion	WWW		116
Fat Face	Fashion	B CO A GQ L CV		60
Fendi	Fashion		W M	123
Féraud Homme	Fashion	B		50
Fila	Sportswear		B	148
Filene's Basement	Fashion		I	131
Fiorelli	Shoes & Accessories	CO		59
Fired Earth Outlet	Home	I		21
Folli Follie	Shoes & Accessories	B	CO	47
Fone Gadgets	Technology	FB		81
Foot Locker	Shoes & Accessories	S		70

KEY TO OUTLETS

B Bicester Village
page 44

Y York
page 52

CO Cheshire Oaks
page 56

A Ashford
page 60

GQ Gunwharf Quays
page 64

S Swindon
page 68

CV Clarks Village
page 72

L Livingstone
page 76

FB Freeport Braintree
page 80

W Whiteley Village
page 84

I Independents UK
page 11

S Sales
page 101

SS Sample Sales
page 107

www Internet Sites
page 113

W Woodbury Common
page 121

CO Citygate Outlet
page 136

B Barberino
page 146

M The Mall
page 150

I International Independents
New York
page 130

Hong Kong
page 135

Florence
page 144

Brand/Retailer	Brand Category	Top 10 Outlet & UK Independents	International & Independents	Page no.
Fornarina	Fashion/Shoes/Accessories		B	148
Fossil	Accessories		W	127
Fox Racing	Outdoor/Sportswear	Y		54
Fox Sport	Sportswear	W		85
Fred Perry	Fashion	B CO A GQ L		50
Freelance Fabrics	Home	I		22
French Connection	Fashion	B GQ	W	127
French Sole Shoes	Shoes & Accessories	I		22
Fressingfield Pottery by Soedergaard Design	Home	I		22
Frette	Home		W B	123
Furla	Accessories	B	W B	50
G-Star Raw	Fashion		W	127
Gaggia	Home	CV FB		72
Gap	Fashion/Children	CO Y A S GQ L CV	W	68
Gas	Fashion		B	148
Geoffrey Beene	Fashion		W	127
Geox	Shoes & Accessories		W	127
Gerard Darel	Fashion	B		47
Ghost	Fashion	GQ		64
Gieves & Hawkes	Fashion	B		47
Giordano	Fashion		CO	138
Giorgio Armani	Fashion	Y	W M	123
Giuseppe Zanotti Design	Shoes & Accessories		W	127
Gleneagles Crystal	Home/Gifts	L		78
Glen Muir	Fashion	I		22
Golden Lady	Fashion		B	148

Brand/Retailer	Brand Category	Top 10 Outlet & UK Independents	International & Independents	Page no.
Godiva Chocolatier	Food		W	127
Goldsmith's	Shoes & Accessories	CO A S		60
Graham and Green	Home	I		22
Greg Norman	Fashion		W	127
Green and Pleasant Interiors	Home	S		70
Grigioperla	Fashion		B	147
Gucci	Fashion/Accessories		W M	124
Guess	Fashion	GQ	W B	66
Guess Accessories	Fashion		W B	127
Guess Kids	Children		B	147
Guru	Fashion		W	148
Gymboree Outlet	Children		B	127
Hackett	Fashion	B Y	W	53
Haggar	Fashion	Y		54
Half Price Perfumes	Beauty	I		23
Hallmark	Gifts	CV		74
Hamleys Outlet	Children	Y S		68
Harrods	Fashion/Shoes Accessories/Home Gifts/Children	S		101
Harry & David	Food		W	127
Hartley Greens Leeds Pottery Ltd	Home	I		23
Hawick Cashmere Company	Fashion	I		23
Hawkshead	Fashion	CV		74
Headline News	Gifts		W	127

Brand/Retailer	Brand Category	Top 10 Outlet & UK Independents	International & Independents	Page no.
Helly Hansen	Sportswear	B		50
Helmut Lang	Fashion		W	127
Henri Lloyd	Fashion	A S CV		62
Hermes	Fashion/Shoes/ Accessories	S		102
Hickey Freeman/ Bobby Jones	Fashion		W	127
High and Mighty	Fashion	W		84
HMV	DVDs, games, music	GQ		66
Hobbs	Fashion	B Y S GQ		50
Hogan	Shoes & Accessories		M	151
Home & Cook	Home	L		78
Home, Curtains & Bedding	Home	S W		85
Hugo Boss	Fashion	B Y	W	50
Hush Puppies	Shoes & Accessories	GQ FB		81
I Pinco Pallino	Children		M	151
Il Lanificio	Fashion		B	148
Intimas Lingerie	Underwear	Y FB		54
IT Outlet	Fashion		CO	138
Izod	Fashion		W	127
Jack Wills	Fashion	B GQ		64
Jacques Vert Group	Fashion	Y CV		54
Jaeger	Fashion	B CO Y S CV W FB I		23
James Gaunt	Home/Fashion	I		23
Jane Shilton	Shoes & Accessories	S CV		70
J Crew	Fashion		W	127
J Crew/ Crewcuts	Children		W	127

Brand/Retailer	Brand Category	Top 10 Outlet & UK Independents	International & Independents	Page no.
Jean's Paul Gaultier	Fashion		B	148
Jeff Banks	Fashion	CV		74
Jeff Banks Studio Store	Fashion	CO Y A		59
Jigsaw	Fashion	B		50
Jill Stuart	Fashion		CO	138
Jimmy Choo	Shoes & Accessories	B	W	47
JJ Brothers Tailors	Fashion		I	135
JM Originals	Children		W	127
Jo Malone	Beauty/Home	I		24
Jockey	Fashion		W	127
Joe's Jeans	Fashion		W	127
Joel & Son Fabrics	Home/Fashion	I		24
John Ashfield	Fashion		B	148
John Jenkins & Sons	Home/Gifts	I S		24
John Lewis	Home/Fashion/ Technology/Gifts	I		24
John Lewis Home Outlet	Home	S		69
John Smedley Ltd	Fashion	I		24
Johnston & Murphy	Shoes & Accessories		W	127
Johnstons of Elgin	Fashion	I S		102
Jones New York	Fashion		W	127
Jones New York Sport & Country	Fashion/Sportswear		W	127
Jones New York Woman	Fashion		W	127
Joseph	Fashion	W I		84
Joules	Fashion	Y CV		54

Brand/Retailer	Brand Category	Top 10 Outlet & UK Independents	International & Independents	Page no.
Journeys	Shoes & Accessories		W	127
Joy & Peace	Fashion		CO	138
Joyce Warehouse	Fashion		I	135
Judith Leiber	Luggage/Accessories/Gifts		W	127
Judith Ripka	Jewellery		W	127
Juicy Couture	Fashion		W	127
Julian Graves	Food	CO Y S L W FB		59
K Swiss	Sportswear/Shoes		CO	138
Karen Millen	Fashion	B CO Y GQ L FB		72
Kangol	Fashion	I		26
Kasper	Fashion		W	127
Kate Spade	Accessories		W CO	124
Kathy Van Zeeland	Accessories		B	148
KB Toy Outlet	Children		W	127
Kenneth Cole	Fashion		W	127
Kenneth Turner	Home/Gifts	B GQ		64
Kensie	Fashion		CO	138
Kent & Curwen	Fashion		CO	138
Kenwood	Home	I		27
KIDS	Children	Y	B	147
Kidderminster Wholesale Carpets	Home	I		27
KingCow	Children		CO	138
Kinji	Fashion		CO	138
Kipling	Luggage/Accessories	B A GQ	W	61
Kitch 'n' Sync	Home	CO		59
Klass	Fashion	Y L W FB		54
Koodos	Fashion	www		114

Brand/Retailer	Brand Category	Top 10 Outlet & UK Independents	International & Independents	Page no.
Krups	Home	S		70
Kurt Geiger	Shoes & Accessories	CO A		57
Kurt Muller	Fashion	CO L FB		77
La Casa Italiana	Home		B	148
La Fuma	Sportswear		CO	138
La Perla	Fashion		W CO	127
La Senza	Underwear	CO CV		59
Lacoste	Fashion/Sports	CO Y A FB	W	80
Lagostina	Home		B	148
Lakeland	Fashion	CO S I		27
Lakeland Leather	Fashion	GQ CV		66
Lancôme - The Company Outlet	Beauty		W	124
Lands End Direct Merchants	Fashion/Outdoor	I		27
Lane Crawford	Fashion/Home/Shoes Accessories/Gifts		I	136
Lanvin	Fashion		CO	138
Laura Ashley	Fashion		CO	138
Le Creuset	Home	CO Y S GQ L CV FB	W	57
Le Saunda	Accessories		CO	138
Lee Cooper	Fashion	CO GQ FB		59
L'eggs Hanes Bali Playtex	Fashion		W	127
Le Gourmet Chef	Home		W	127
Lenox	Home		W	127
Lens Crafters	Accessories		CO	138
Les Copains	Fashion		B	148
LeSportsac	Accessories		W	127
Levi's	Fashion	B CO Y A S L	B CO	50

Brand/Retailer	Brand Category	Top 10 Outlet & UK Independents	International & Independents	Page no.
Levi's/Dockers Outlet by Most	Fashion		W	127
Levi Strauss	Fashion	GQ		66
Lids for Less	Accessories		W	127
Lilley & Skinner	Shoes & Accessories	CO A S L W FB		59
Lillywhites	Sportswear	CV W		84
Links of London	Shoes & Accessories	B		47
Linton Tweeds Ltd	Fashion	I		28
Lipsy Clothing	Fashion	FB		82
Liz Claiborne	Fashion	GQ	W	65
LK Bennett	Fashion/ Shoes	B Y S GQ I		28
Lladró	Gifts		W	127
Lloyd Loom of Spalding	Home	I		28
L'Occitane	Beauty	B GQ	W	65
Loehmann's	Fashion		I	131
Logo	Fashion	CO Y A L		59
Lolapalooza	Fashion/Home	SS		109
Lombok Clearance & White Company	Home	I		28
London Accessory Sale	Accessories	SS		108
London Fashion Weekend	Accessories	SS		107
Longchamp	Accessories		W	124
L'Oréal	Beauty	B		50
Loro Piana	Fashion	B	W M	47
Lovable Playtex Planet	Fashion		B	148
Lucky Brand Jeans	Fashion		W	127
Luella	Fashion	B		48

Brand/Retailer	Brand Category	Top 10 Outlet & UK Independents	International & Independents	Page no.
Luxury Beauty Store	Beauty	L		78
Madhouse	Fashion	W		85
Magic Mountain	Sportswear/Outdoor	I		28
Maidenform	Fashion		W	127
Malloy	Fashion		B	148
Malo	Fashion/Accessories		B	147
Mamas & Papas	Children/Fashion	I		29
Mambo	Fashion	GQ		66
Margaret Howell	Fashion	Y		53
Mariella Burani	Fashion/Accessories		B	148
Mark Marengo Fashion	Fashion	W		86
Marks & Spencer	Fashion/Home/Children	CO Y A S GQ L CV FB		59
Marlboro Classic	Fashion/Accessories		B	148
Marni	Fashion		M	151
Marston & Langinger	Home	I		29
Marshall Leisure Ltd	Sportswear/Outdoor	I		29
Massimo Rebecchi	Fashion		B	148
Matthew Williamson	Fashion	B		48
Maui Bear	Fashion/Shoes/Accessories		B	148
MaxMara	Fashion	B	M	124
MaxStudio.com	Fashion		W	127
Me Belle	Accessories		CO	138
Merchants Fine Jewellery	Jewellry	L		78
Mexx	Fashion/ Children	B CO Y A GQ L FB		50
Michael Cooper's Studio	Art/Gifts	CV		74

Brand/Retailer	Brand Category	Top 10 Outlet & UK Independents	International & Independents	Page no.
Michael Kors	Fashion/Accessories		W	124
Mira Belle	Accessories		CO	138
Missoni	Fashion		W B	124
Miss Sixty/Energie	Fashion	B	W	48
Moiselle	Fashion		CO	138
Molton Brown	Shoes & Accessories	B CO GQ		57
Money Saving Expert	General	www		114
Monsoon	Fashion	B CO GQ CV		50
Montane	Outdoor	I		29
Mooche	Beauty	Y		54
Moorcroft Pottery	Home/Gifts	I		31
Moreschi	Shoes & Accessories		B	148
Moss/ Moss Bros Hire	Fashion	CO Y A S L W FB		59
Motivi	Fashion/Accessories		B	148
Motostore	Sportswear		B	148
Moulinex	Home	S		70
Mountain Warehouse	Sportswear/Outdoor	CO Y A S GQ L CV FB		81
Movado Company Store	Accessories		W	127
Mulberry	Shoes & Accessories	B		50
Mulberry Factory Shop	Shoes & Accessories	I		31
Multiyork	Home	I		31
Musto	Sports	B L		69
Myla	Underwear	B		50
My-Wardrobe.com	Fashion	www		116
N Peal	Fashion	B		50

Brand/Retailer	Brand Category	Top 10 Outlet & UK Independents	International & Independents	Page no.
Nathan Road, Kowloon	Technology		I	136
Naturalizer	Shoes & Accessories		W	127
Nautica	Fashion/Sportswear		W B CO	127
NauticaKids	Children		W	127
Neiman Marcus Last Call	Fashion/ Home		W	124
Net-A-Porter	Fashion/Shoes/ Accessories	WWW		115
New Balance	Sportswear		CO	138
New Balance Athletics Shoes Ltd	Sportswear/Shoes	I		31
New Era Cap	Fashion	FB		82
Next Clearance	Fashion/Children	CO Y A S GQ L CV FB		59
Nicholas Mosse	Home	I		32
Nicole Farhi	Fashion	B		48
Nike	Sportswear	GQ FB	CO	138
Nike Factory Store	Sportswear	CO A S L CV	W	57
Nine West	Shoes & Accessories		W	127
Nitya	Fashion	B CO Y GQ L		50
O2	Technology	Y		54
Oakley	Fashion/Sportswear	GQ		65
Oakley Vault	Fashion/Sportswear	Y	W	127
Oasis	Fashion	CO A GQ L		59
Officina Di Ricerca	Fashion		B	148
OKA Discount Shop	Home	I		32
Olsen	Fashion	Y S L		54
O'Neill	Sportswear/Outdoor	GQ		66
Oneida	Home	CO Y GQ CV		54
Optical 88	Accessories		CO	138

Brand/Retailer	Brand Category	Top 10 Outlet & UK Independents	International & Independents	Page no.
Orange	Technology	FB		82
Orvis	Fashion	CV		72
Oscar de la Renta	Fashion		W	125
OshKosh B'Gosh	Children		W	125
Outdoor Project	Outdoor	W		86
Outdoor Scene	Outdoor	L		78
Ozwald Boateng	Fashion	B		48
PJ Bridgman	Home	I		32
PacSun	Sportswear/Outdoor		W	127
Pal Zileri	Fashion		B	148
Paperchase	Gifts/Stationery	GQ		65
Pascal Jewellery	Jewellery	B		50
Past Times	Home/Gifts	CV W FB		84
Paul Costelloe Factory Store	Fashion	I		32
Paul Smith	Fashion	B Y GQ		50
Pavers Outlet	Shoes & Accessories	Y W		54
Pedder Warehouse	Accessories		CO	138
Penhaligon's	Beauty	B Y		53
Perfumania	Beauty		W	127
Perfume Point	Beauty	CO Y A L		77
Perry Ellis	Fashion		W	127
Peruvian Connection	Fashion/Accessories	I		33
Petit Bateau	Children	B		50
Petroleum	Fashion	CO Y A S L W FB		59
Phase Eight	Fashion	A S		69
Phones 4 U	Technology	L		78
Pilgrim	Accessories	CO		59

Brand/Retailer	Brand Category	Top 10 Outlet & UK Independents	International & Independents	Page no.
Pilot	Fashion	CO S W FB		59
Pinko	Fashion		B	148
Piquardo	Accessories		B	148
Playtex/Gossard/ Wonderbra	Underwear	CO A GQ L FB		59
Playtime	Children	CO		59
Pollini	Shoes & Accessories		B	148
Polo Ralph Lauren	Fashion	B CO Y A S GQ		61
Polo Ralph Lauren Children	Children		W CO	127
Ponden Mill	Home	CO S GQ CV W FB		59
Portmeirion	Home	S CV I		33
Prada (also see Space)	Fashion		W B I	125
Pratesi	Home		W	125
Price's Candles	Home/Gifts	CV W		85
Prima Designer Clothing	Fashion	Y CV		54
Prima Designer Man	Fashion	CO		59
Prima Tessuti	Fashion	CO		59
Principles	Fashion	A		61
Pringle Factory Shop	Fashion	I		33
Pringle of Scotland	Fashion	B CO		50
Professional Cookware Co.	Home	CO Y A S GQ L CV FB		61
Proudfoot Leather and Lambskin	Fashion	FB		82
Puma	Sportswear	B CO A S GQ	W B CO	50
Pumpkin Patch	Children	S		70
Pupa Outlet	Beauty		B	148

Brand/Retailer	Brand Category	Top 10 Outlet & UK Independents	International & Independents	Page no.
Q Come Quore	Children		B	148
Quiksilver	Sportswear/ Outdoor	B S	W CO	50
Rabeanco	Accessories		CO	138
Racing Green	Fashion	B CO Y A CV FB		81
Radley	Shoes & Accessories	B		50
Ralph Lauren Home	Home		W	127
Ravel	Shoes & Accessories	Y		54
RCR-Royal Crystal Rock	Home/Gifts		B	148
Reebok	Sports	B CO Y A L FB	W	53
Reef	Fashion/Outdoor	GQ		66
Regatta	Outdoor	L FB		78
Remington	Beauty	CO Y GQ		59
Replay Factory Outlet	Fashion	I		33
Revlon	Beauty	CO A L		61
Reiss	Fashion	B		50
Richmond	Fashion		B	148
Rifle	Fashion		B	148
Rip Curl	Fashion/Outdoor	GQ		66
Robe Di Kappa	Fashion/Sportswear/ Children		B	148
Roberto Cavalli	Fashion		W I	125
Roberto Cavalli Class	Fashion		B	148
Rocco Bormioli	Home/Gifts		B	148
Rochester Big & Tall	Fashion		W	127
Rock Couture	Fashion	B		50
Rockford Footwear Depot	Shoes & Accessories		W	127
Rockport	Shoes & Accessories	CO	W CO	127

Brand/Retailer	Brand Category	Top 10 Outlet & UK Independents	International & Independents	Page no.
Rohan	Fashion/Outdoor	CV FB		73
Roman Originals	Fashion	CO Y A GQ L CV W FB		59
Room	Home	W		86
Roots	Fashion		CO	138
Rowenta	Home	S		70
Royal Crown Derby	Pottery	I		34
Royal Doulton	Home		W	127
Royal Worcester	Home	CO I		34
Royal Worcester & Spode	Home	CV		74
Ruby and Roses	Home	CV		74
Rugs Plus	Home	Y L		54
Rug Traders	Home	S		70
Saks Fifth Avenue Off 5th	Fashion/Shoes		W	127
Saltrock	Fashion/Outdoor	CV		74
Salvatore Ferragamo	Fashion/Shoes	B	W M	48
Sam's Tailor	Fashion		I	136
Samsonite	Luggage	B CO A S L W FB	W CO	81
Sand	Fashion	B Y		50
Sandpiper Books	Books	I		34
Sanderson Clearance Outlet Shop	Home	I		34
Sarar	Fashion		W	127
Sasperilla	Fashion	FB		82
Savoy Taylors Guild	Fashion	B GQ CV FB		73
Secret Sales	Fashion	WWW		102
Segue	Shoes & Accessories		B	148
Seiko The Company Store	Jewellry		W	127

Brand/Retailer	Brand Category	Top 10 Outlet & UK Independents	International & Independents	Page no.
Select	Fashion	(L) (W)		78
Sergio Rossi	Shoes & Accessories		(M)	151
Seven7	Fashion		(CO)	138
Shoe Studio	Shoes & Accessories	(Y)		54
Shoon	Shoes & Accessories	(S)		69
Sia	Home		(B)	148
Sketchers	Shoes & Accessories	(CO) (L)	(W)	127
Slam	Sportswear		(B)	148
Smythson	Stationery/Accessories	(S)		103
Soft Shoe Co.	Shoes & Accessories	(Y)		54
Soled Out	Shoes & Accessories	(CO) (A) (L) (FB)		59
Solstice Sunglass Outlet	Accessories		(W)	127
Sonex presents Sony	Technology	(CV)		74
Sony	Technology/Gifts		(W)	127
Sony Playstation	Technology		(B)	148
Southern Domestic Electrical Services	Home/Electricals	(I)		34
Space (Prada)	Fashion/Accessories		(W) (M) (I)	127
Space NK	Beauty	(S)		70
Specs & Lenses	Accessories	(FB)		82
Speedo International Ltd	Sportswear	(I)		36
Spode	Home	(I)		36
Spyder	Sportswear		(W)	127
St Diego - A-tyle	Fashion		(B)	148
St. John Company Store	Fashion		(W)	125
Staccato Fashion Footwear	Shoes & Accessories	(Y) (A) (FB)		54

Brand/Retailer	Brand Category	Top 10 Outlet & UK Independents	International & Independents	Page no.
Stefanel	Fashion		B	148
Stella McCartney	Fashion		M	150
Stone	Jewellry	CV FB		74
Stone Island/Evisu	Fashion	S		70
Store House	Fashion		B	148
Stride Rite Keds Sperry	Shoes & Accessories		W	127
Stuart Crystal	Home	I		36
Studio Moda	Fashion	B		50
Suits You/ Young's Hire	Fashion	CO Y A S GQ L CV FB		59
Sunglass Hut	Accessories		W	127
Sunglass Station	Accessories		W	127
Sunglass Time	Accessories	B CO Y A S GQ L CV	B	77
Swarovski	Accessories		W	125
TAG Heuer	Accessories	B	W	48
Tahari	Fashion		W	127
Tailor Club	Fashion		B	148
Ted Baker	Fashion	B CO Y A S GQ L FB		77
Tefal	Home	Y S		69
Temperley London	Fashion	B		48
That Great Food Place	Food	GQ		66
The Body Shop	Beauty		CO	138
The Body Shop Depot	Beauty	Y CV		73
The Bridge	Acessories		B	148
The British Designer Sale		SS		103
The Children's Place Outlet	Children		W	127

Brand/Retailer	Brand Category	Top 10 Outlet & UK Independents	International & Independents	Page no.
The Cosmetics Company Store	Beauty	B CO GQ	W	50
The Designer Studio	Fashion	Y L		54
The Edinburgh Woollen Mill	Fashion	CV		74
The End	Fashion		B	148
The Gadget Company UK	Gifts	GQ		66
The London Jewelry Collection	Jewellry		W	128
The Luggage Factory	Luggage		W	128
The Luxury Beauty Store	Beauty	S		70
The North Face	Sportswear/Outdoor	B CO	W	128
The Paper Mill Shop	Gifts/Stationery	CO Y A S GQ L CV W FB		59
The Perfume Shop	Beauty	GQ CV FB		66
The Real Flower Company	Gifts	I		36
The Really Good Deal Fashion Sale	Fashion/Gifts/Home	SS		109
The Secret Sample Sale	Fashion	SS		110
The Siteguide.com		www		116
The White Company	Home	B		49
The Works	Books/ Home	GQ L CV		66
Theory	Fashion		W CO	128
Theory Men	Fashion		W	125
Thomas Pink	Fashion	B Y S	W	69
Thorntons	Food/Gifts	CO Y S GQ CV		59
Threshers Wine Rack	Food/Gifts	I		37

Brand/Retailer	Brand Category	Top 10 Outlet & UK Independents	International & Independents	Page no.
Timberland	Fashion	B CO Y S GQ CV	W B CO	53
Time Out	Fashion	WWW		116
Time & Style	Accessories		CO	138
Time Factory Watch Outlet	Accessories		W	128
TK Maxx	Fashion/Home/Shoes Accessories/Gifts	I		37
TM Lewin	Fashion	CO A GQ		61
Toast	Fashion/Home	I		37
Tod's	Shoes & Accessories	B	W M	49
Tog 24 Outdoor Clothing	Sports	B CO Y A S GQ L CV I		37
Tommy Bahama	Fashion/Home		W	128
Tommy Hilfiger	Fashion	B CO Y A S FB		57
Tommy Kids	Children		W	128
Top Table	Home	W		85
Tor Stone	Home	CV		74
Tory Burch	Fashion/Sportswear		W	125
Toshiba	Home	CO A		59
Totes/Isotoners/ Sunglass World	Accessories		W	128
Trade Secret	Home	I		37
Trade Secret Hairdressers and Shop	Beauty	GQ		66
Travel Accessory	Accessories	Y		54
Trespass	Outdoor	L CV W FB		85
Triumph	Fashion	CO S GQ CV	CO	138
Tripp	Accessories	CO		59
True Religion	Fashion		W	126
TSE Cashmere	Fashion	B	W	49

Brand/Retailer	Brand Category	Top 10 Outlet & UK Independents	International & Independents	Page no.
Tula	Accessories	CO A S GQ L CV FB		59
Tumi	Luggage	B	W	49
Tutta Bella, Nails & Beauty	Beauty	S		70
Ugg	Shoes & Accessories		W	126
Ugo Colella	Fashion		B	148
Ultra Diamonds	Jewellry		W	128
Under Armour	Sportswear		W	128
United Colours of Benetton	Fashion		B	148
Urban	Sportswear/Outdoor	L		78
Urban Junkies		WWW		116
Vecopri	Children	Y		54
Valentino	Fashion		W M	126
Vallebona Ltd	Food/Gifts	I		38
Van Heusen	Fashion	CO Y A S L CV FB	W	73
Vans	Fashion	B CO GQ		50
Versace	Fashion	B		49
Vestebene	Fashion		B	148
Victorinox Swiss Army	Gifts		W	126
Vilebrequin	Fashion	B		50
Villeroy & Boch	Home	B CO GQ FB		57
Vineyard Vines	Fashion/Sportswear		W	128
Virgin Cosmetics Company Store	Beauty	CO Y L		77
Vitamin World	Health		W	128
Vivienne Tam	Fashion		CO	138
Viyella	Fashion	Y		54

Brand/Retailer	Brand Category	Top 10 Outlet & UK Independents	International & Independents	Page no.
Vodafone	Technology	CV		74
Volga Linen	Home	I		38
Warehouse	Fashion	CO		59
Waterford Wedgwood	Home	B S CV FB I	W	38
Wedgwood	Home	CO I		39
Wesley Barrell	Home	I		39
Whistles	Fashion	B GQ		50
WH Smith	Gifts	CO		59
White Stuff	Fashion	GQ CV		73
Whittard of Chelsea	Home/Gifts	CO Y A S GQ L CV W FB		85
Williams-Sonoma Outlet	Home		W	126
Winchester Village Furniture	Home	W		86
Windsmoor	Fashion	CO L CV		59
Winning Line	Fashion	CO		59
Wolford	Underwear	B	W	49
Wolsey	Fashion	Y		54
World Belts	Shoes & Accessories	S		70
World of Fun	Children		W	128
Wrangler - Lee	Fashion		B	148
Yankee Candle	Home/Gifts	S	W	70
Yohji Yamamoto	Fashion		M	151
Yves Saint Laurent	Fashion		M	151
Yves Saint Laurent Rive Gauche	Fashion		W	126
Zales Outlet	Jewellry		W	128
Zavvi	DVDs, games, music	S L CV FB		70
Zegna	Fashion		M	150

Photo Credit Listing

Page 76
Sloane Street Shop front

Page 79
Shirts, **TM Lewin**, page 61

Page 83
Sushi, **ITSU**, 16 Locations in London. www.itsu.co.uk

Page 85
Shits and Tie, **Hackett**, page 53

Page 87
Large Vase, **John Jenkins**, page 34

Page 90
Belt, **Malo**, page 147

Page 95
Tuna, **Vallebona**, page 38.
Cups, **Chomette**, page15

Page 99
Men's Sweaters, **Johnston's of Elgin**, page 102

Page 103
Baby Cashmere Sweater, **Hermes Sale**, page 102

Page 104
Stationery, **Smythson**, page 103

Page 109
Cashmere Rug, **Johnston's of Elgin**, page 102.
Hermes Sale Shopping Bag, page 102

Page 111
Shopping Bags, Various Outlets.

Acknowledgements

Firstly, I'd like to thank my employer, Lady Gosling, whose help and generous support enabled me to spend the time necessary to put together How to Shop. I also owe a huge debt of thanks to the designer Mandy Sherliker, the creative force behind this book.

A very big big 'thank you' is also owed to the How to Shop team – Alison, Amy, Emma, Georgina, Hannah and Suzy whose many hours of detailed research and verification has made our book what, I believe, is the best shopping guide money can buy.

Thanks are also owed to the creative team – Chris, Danny, Jane, Leah, Nick, Ruth, our print consultant Philip Chippindale, our publishing advisor Jane Slater, and Keiko, our photographer, whose fantastic photographs feature throughout the book.

The services of the professional advisor team are also to be thanked. Finally, many thanks to all those people who have supported How to Shop and, most importantly, to you for purchasing a copy.